INTEGRATION OF ORDINARY DIFFERENTIAL EQUATIONS

UNIVERSITY MATHEMATICAL TEXTS

GENERAL EDITORS

ALEXANDER C. AITKEN, D.SC., F.R.S.
DANIEL E. RUTHERFORD, D.SC., DR.MATH.

Determinants and Matrices	A. C. Aitken, D.Sc., F.R.S.
Statistical Mathematics	A. C. Aitken, D.Sc., F.R.S.
The Theory of Ordinary Differential Equations	J. C. Burkill, Sc.D., F.R.S.
Waves	C. A. Coulson, D.Sc., F.R.S.
Electricity	C. A. Coulson, D.Sc., F.R.S.
Projective Geometry	T. E. Faulkner, Ph.D.
Integration	R. P. Gillespie, Ph.D.
Partial Differentiation	R. P. Gillespie, Ph.D.
Real Variable	J. M. Hyslop, D.Sc.
Infinite Series	J. M. Hyslop, D.Sc.
Integration of Ordinary Differential Equations	E. L. Ince, D.Sc.
Introduction to the Theory of Finite Groups	W. Ledermann, Ph.D., D.Sc.
German-English Mathematical Vocabulary	S. Macintyre, Ph.D., and E. Witte, M.A.
Analytical Geometry of Three Dimensions	W. H. McCrea, Ph.D., F.R.S.
Russian Reader in Pure and Applied Mathematics	P. H. Nidditch, Ph.D.
Topology	E. M. Patterson, Ph.D.
Functions of a Complex Variable	E. G. Phillips, M.A., M.Sc.
Special Relativity	W. Rindler, Ph.D.
Volume and Integral	W. W. Rogosinski, Dr. Phil., F.R.S.
Vector Methods	D. E. Rutherford, D.Sc., Dr.Math.
Classical Mechanics	D. E. Rutherford, D.Sc., Dr.Math.
Fluid Dynamics	D. E. Rutherford, D.Sc., Dr.Math.
Special Functions of Mathematical Physics and Chemistry	I. N. Sneddon, D.Sc.
Tensor Calculus	B. Spain, Ph.D.
Theory of Equations	H. W. Turnbull, F.R.S.

INTEGRATION OF ORDINARY DIFFERENTIAL EQUATIONS

BY

E. L. INCE, D.Sc.

LECTURER IN TECHNICAL MATHEMATICS IN THE UNIVERSITY OF EDINBURGH
FORMERLY PROFESSOR OF PURE MATHEMATICS IN THE EGYPTIAN UNIVERSITY

SEVENTH EDITION—REVISED

OLIVER AND BOYD
EDINBURGH AND LONDON
NEW YORK: INTERSCIENCE PUBLISHERS INC.

FIRST EDITION	.	1939
SECOND EDITION	.	1943
THIRD EDITION	.	1944
FOURTH EDITION	.	1946
FIFTH EDITION	.	1949
SIXTH EDITION	.	1952
SEVENTH EDITION	.	1956
REPRINTED	.	1959, 1963

PRINTED AND PUBLISHED IN GREAT BRITAIN BY
OLIVER AND BOYD LTD., EDINBURGH

PREFACE

THE object of this book is to provide in a compact form an account of the methods of integrating explicitly the commoner types of ordinary differential equation, and in particular those equations that arise from problems in geometry and applied mathematics. It takes the existence of solutions for granted; the reader who desires to look into the theoretical background of the methods here outlined will find what he seeks in my larger treatise *Ordinary Differential Equations* (Longmans, Green & Co., Ltd., 1927). With this qualification, it will be found to contain all the material needed by students in our Universities who do not specialize in differential equations, as well as by students of mathematical physics and technology.

As one of the first things a beginner has to learn is to identify the type to which a given equation belongs, the examples for solution have not been printed after the sections to which they refer, but have been collected at the end of the book. When the contents of the first chapter have been mastered, the reader may test his skill by attacking examples selected at random from Nos. 1 to 122, and similarly for the later chapters. The examples occur roughly in the order of the table of contents, so that working material is always available as reading progresses.

In conclusion, I wish to record my thanks to the General Editors for their encouragement and help during its growth and passage through the press.

May 1939 E. L. I.

The Second Edition, through the untimely death of the author in March 1941, has not had the advantage of being revised by him. The Editors are indebted to Dr I. M. H. Etherington and Miss N. Walls for some corrections, and to Dr A. Erdélyi for undertaking a scrutiny of the book and recasting parts of Chapter VI.

A. C. A.

April 1943 D. E. R.

CONTENTS

CHAPTER I

EQUATIONS OF THE FIRST ORDER AND DEGREE

CHAPTER II

INTEGRAL CURVES

CHAPTER III

EQUATIONS OF HIGHER DEGREE

CHAPTER IV

EQUATIONS OF THE SECOND AND HIGHER ORDERS

CHAPTER V

LINEAR EQUATIONS

CHAPTER VI

SOLUTION IN SERIES

CHAPTER I

EQUATIONS OF THE FIRST ORDER AND DEGREE

1. Definitions. Let x be an independent, and y a dependent variable; let $y', y'', \ldots, y^{(n)}$ represent successive derivatives of y with respect to x. Then any relation of equality which involves at least one of these derivatives is said to be an *ordinary differential equation.* The term *ordinary* distinguishes it from a *partial* differential equation, which would involve two or more independent variables, a dependent variable, and the corresponding partial derivatives. The *order* of any differential equation is the order of the highest derivative involved. Thus any relation of the form

$$F(x, y, y', y'', \ldots, y^{(n)}) = 0$$

is an ordinary differential equation of order n.

Differential equations, both ordinary and partial, are of frequent occurrence in mechanics and mathematical physics, but the illustrations that best serve to introduce the subject are taken from the geometry of plane curves.

The equation

$$f(x, y, C) = 0, \quad . \quad . \quad . \quad (1.1)$$

in which x and y are rectangular co-ordinates and C is a parameter or arbitrary constant, represents a family of curves, in which one curve corresponds to one value of C, another curve to another value. If, regarding C for the moment as fixed, we differentiate with respect to x, we obtain

$$\frac{\partial f}{\partial x} + \frac{\partial f}{\partial y} y' = 0. \quad . \quad . \quad . \quad (1.2)$$

Generally speaking, (1.2) will involve C; if C is eliminated between the two equations, there will result an equation involving x, y, and y', say

$$F(x, y, y') = 0, \qquad (1.3)$$

that is, an ordinary differential equation *of the first order*. When such an equation is polynomial in y' (but not necessarily in x and y) the index of the highest power of y' involved is said to be the *degree* of the equation.

Geometrically, the differential equation (1.3) implies that at any chosen point of the (x, y)-plane the derivative has a certain value or values, that is to say it symbolizes a property of the gradient of any curve of the family (1.1) that passes through the point (x, y) considered.

Example 1. The equation

$$y = x^2 + C$$

represents a family of equal parabolas having the y-axis as their common axis. On differentiating with respect to x we have

$$y' = 2x.$$

The arbitrary constant C has disappeared, so that this is actually the differential equation of the family of parabolas. It expresses the fact that all the curves of the family have the same gradient at the points where they are cut by a line parallel to the y-axis, namely a gradient equal to twice the abscissa of the line.

Example 2. The equation

$$y = Cx^2$$

represents a family of similar parabolas having the y-axis as their common axis, and all touching the x-axis at the origin. Differentiating, we obtain

$$y' = 2Cx,$$

which involves C; if this constant is eliminated we obtain the differential equation

$$y' = 2y/x,$$

and has the general integral

$$\int\frac{M(x)}{S(x)}dx+\int\frac{N(y)}{R(y)}dy=C.$$

When, as in the above cases, the process leads to an expression that involves integral signs the result is said to be an *integration by quadratures*. This implies that the problem has been reduced from one in differential equations to an equivalent in the integral calculus. If it is found impossible to evaluate one or other of the integrals, an explicit solution of the equation is impossible, and the solution by quadratures must be regarded as the best attainable, unless an alternative line of approach can be discovered.

Example 1.

$$x(y^2-1)dx-y(x^2-1)dy=0.$$

Separating the variables:

$$\frac{xdx}{x^2-1}-\frac{ydy}{y^2-1}=0.$$

Integrating,

$$\log|x^2-1|-\log|y^2-1|=C$$

or

$$\log\left|\frac{x^2-1}{y^2-1}\right|=-\log c$$

which may be written

$$(y^2-1)=c(x^2-1).$$

(Note that replacing the arbitrary constant C by another arbitrary form, as in this case $C=-\log c$, may help to simplify the general integral.)

Example 2.

$$\frac{dx}{\sqrt{(1-x^2)}}+\frac{dy}{\sqrt{(1-y^2)}}=0.$$

The variables are separate; direct integration gives

$$\text{arc sin } x+\text{arc sin } y=C$$

which is the general integral. This may be transformed into an equivalent expression by slightly rearranging the terms and taking the sine of both members, thus:

$$\sin\{\text{arc}\sin y\} = \sin\{C - \text{arc}\sin x\}$$

or, since

$$\cos\{\text{arc}\sin x\} = \pm\sqrt{(1-x^2)},$$
$$y = \pm\sqrt{(1-x^2)}\sin C - x\cos C$$

and, rationalising,

$$(y + x\cos C)^2 = (1-x^2)\sin^2 C,$$

i.e.

$$x^2 + y^2 + 2xy\cos C = \sin^2 C$$

or, if $c = \cos C$,

$$x^2 + y^2 + 2cxy = 1 - c^2.$$

Example 3. A change in variables may sometimes succeed in converting an equation into another with separate variables. For instance, in

$$(x+y)dx + dy = 0$$

the variables are not separable, but if y is replaced by $v - x$, the equation is transformed into

$$(v-1)dx + dv = 0.$$

The variables x and v are separable, thus

$$dx + \frac{dv}{v-1} = 0$$

which leads to

$$x + \log|v-1| = \log c \quad \text{or} \quad (v-1)e^x = c$$

so that the original equation has a general integral of the form

$$(x+y-1)e^x = c, \quad \text{or} \quad y = ce^{-x} - x + 1.$$

The most important instance of reduction by change of variables occurs in the case of the homogeneous equation which now follows.

4. The Homogeneous Type. The equation

$$P(x, y)dx + Q(x, y)dy = 0$$

is said to be of homogeneous type when P and Q are homogeneous functions of x and y *of the same degree.* If the degree is m, the substitution $y = vx$ will reduce P and Q to the forms

$$P(x, vx) = x^m R(v), \qquad Q(x, vx) = x^m S(v),$$

where R and S are independent of x. Thus the factor x^m may be cancelled out of the equation, which becomes

$$R(v)dx + S(v)\{vdx + xdv\} = 0$$

or

$$\{R(v) + vS(v)\}dx + xS(v)dv = 0.$$

Separating the variables and integrating, we have

$$\int \frac{S(v)dv}{R(v) + vS(v)} + \log x = C,$$

and when the integral in v has been evaluated, the substitution $v = y/x$ will give the general integral of the original equation.

Example 1.

$$(x^2 - y^2)dx + 2xydy = 0.$$

The two terms in this equation are homogeneous and of the second degree in x and y; the above process is therefore applicable. Making the substitution mentioned, we have

$$x^2(1 - v^2)dx + 2x^2v(vdx + xdv) = 0;$$

x^2 cancels out, leaving

$$(1 + v^2)dx + 2vxdv = 0.$$

Separating variables and integrating:

$$\int \frac{2vdv}{1 + v^2} + \int \frac{dx}{x} = C$$

or

$$\log(1 + v^2) + \log x = \log c,$$

i.e.

$$(1 + v^2)x = c$$

which leads to the general integral

$$x^2 + y^2 = cx.$$

Example 2.

$$(2ye^{y/x} - x)y' + 2x + y = 0.$$

Here each term is of the first degree in x and y, for $e^{y/x}$ is of degree zero. Writing $y=vx$, $y'=xv'+v$ and cancelling x, we obtain

$$(2ve^v-1)xv'+2(v^2e^v+1)=0.$$

Separating the variables, this becomes

$$\frac{2v-e^{-v}}{v^2+e^{-v}}dv+\frac{2dx}{x}=0.$$

Integrating, we have

$$\log(v^2+e^{-v})+2\log x=C,$$

whence the general integral

$$y^2+x^2e^{-y/x}=c.$$

5. The Equation with Linear Coefficients. Although the equation

$$(ax+by+c)dx+(a'x+b'y+c')dy=0 \quad . \quad (5.1)$$

is not of homogeneous type, it may be reduced to that type by a simple substitution. The equations

$$ax+by+c=0, \qquad a'x+b'y+c'=0 \quad . \quad (5.2)$$

represent a pair of straight lines which will intersect unless the condition for parallelism, *i.e.* $a'/a=b'/b$ or $ab'-a'b=0$, is satisfied. Let (h, k) be the point of intersection; transfer the origin to that point by the substitution

$$x=h+X, \qquad y=k+Y$$

and the equation will become

$$(aX+bY)dX+(a'X+b'Y)dY=0.$$

It is now homogeneous; the substitution $Y=vX$ followed by separation of variables leads to the general integral

$$\log CX+\int\frac{(a'+b'v)dv}{a+(a'+b)v+b'v^2}=0,$$

whose ultimate form * depends upon whether the roots

* For which see § 17 *infra*.

of the denominator of the integrand are real, coincident or imaginary, *i.e.* according as $(a'+b)^2$ is greater than, equal to, or less than $4ab'$.

In the exceptional case when the lines (5.2) are parallel, that is when $a'/a=b'/b=k$ (say), the equation can be written

$$(ax+by+c)dx+\{k(ax+by)+c'\}dy=0.$$

Take $z=ax+by$ as a new variable to replace y, then

$$b(z+c)dx+(kz+c')(dz-adx)=0.$$

Separating the variables and integrating, we have

$$x+\int\frac{(kz+c')dz}{(b-ak)z+bc-ac'}=\text{const.}$$

The above are particular cases of an equation of the type

$$y'=F\left(\frac{ax+by+c}{a'x+b'y+c'}\right)$$

which may be reduced to a form integrable by quadratures by the same routine process.

Example 1.

$$y'=\frac{4x-y+7}{2x+y-1}.$$

The lines $4x-y+7=0$, $2x+y-1=0$ meet in $(-1, 3)$; writing $x=X-1$, $y=Y+3$ we have

$$(2X+Y)dY=(4X-Y)dX.$$

The transformation $Y=vX$ reduces this equation to

$$(2+v)Xdv+(v^2+3v-4)dX=0$$

which becomes, on separating the variables and taking partial fractions,

$$\left\{\frac{3}{v-1}+\frac{2}{v+4}\right\}dv+\frac{5dX}{X}=0.$$

Integrating,

$$3\log|v-1|+2\log|v+4|+5\log|X|=C,$$

i.e.

$$(v-1)^3(v+4)^2X^5=c$$

or

$$(Y-X)^3(Y+4X)^2=c.$$

Reverting to the variables x, y we have the general integral

$$(y-x-4)^3(y+4x+1)^2=c.$$

Example 2.

$$(2x-4y+5)y'+x-2y+3=0.$$

If $z=x-2y$, $2y'=1-z'$; with this transformation the equation becomes

$$(2z+5)z'=4z+11.$$

Separating the variables, we obtain

$$\left(1-\frac{1}{4z+11}\right)dz=2dx$$

whence

$$4z-\log|4z+11|=8x-C,$$

giving the general integral

$$4x+8y+\log|4x-8y+11|=C.$$

6. Exact Equations. When the primitive of a differential equation involves the arbitrary constant C explicitly, as:

$$u(x, y)=C, \quad . \quad . \quad . \quad (6.1)$$

the operation of taking the differential eliminates C automatically, thus:

$$du(x, y)=0 \quad . \quad . \quad . \quad (6.2)$$

or

$$\frac{\partial u}{\partial x}dx+\frac{\partial u}{\partial y}dy=0. \quad . \quad . \quad . \quad (6.3)$$

Conversely, if a differential equation of the form

$$P(x, y)dx+Q(x, y)dy=0 \quad . \quad . \quad (6.4)$$

has originated in such a process, and if no variable factor has been cancelled out, it must be equivalent to one of the form (6.3) and thus to (6.2), and therefore it must possess a general integral of the form (6.1). Such an equation is said to be *exact*.

Thus, in order that (6.4) may be exact, there must exist a function $u(x, y)$ such that

$$P(x, y) = \frac{\partial u}{\partial x}, \qquad Q(x, y) = \frac{\partial u}{\partial y} \quad . \quad . \quad (6.5)$$

and therefore

$$\frac{\partial P}{\partial y} = \frac{\partial^2 u}{\partial x \partial y} = \frac{\partial Q}{\partial x}.$$

Hence the theorem: *for the differential equation* (6.4) *to be exact it is necessary that* $P(x, y)$ *and* $Q(x, y)$ *be linked by the relation*

$$\frac{\partial P}{\partial y} = \frac{\partial Q}{\partial x}. \quad . \quad . \quad . \quad (6.6)$$

This is known as the *condition of integrability,** for when it is satisfied the primitive $u(x, y) = C$ can be recovered by the following process. Starting from the relation

$$\frac{\partial u(x, y)}{\partial x} = P(x, y),$$

integrating and remembering that since the differentiation with respect to x was partial, the inverse process of integration will introduce, as the arbitrary element, a function of y, we have,

$$\begin{aligned} u(x, y) &= \int P(x, y)dx + \phi(y) \\ &= S(x, y) + \phi(y) \qquad \text{(say).} \end{aligned}$$

But, on the other hand,

$$Q(x, y) = \frac{\partial u}{\partial y} = \frac{\partial S}{\partial y} + \phi'(y),$$

an equation which will give $\phi'(y)$ since Q and S are both known; the final integration to obtain $\phi(y)$ will introduce the arbitrary constant C of the general integral.

* Immediate integrability is implied; when the condition is not satisfied, the equation is still integrable, though not without some preliminary manipulation.

Example 1.

$$\frac{(1+y^2)ydx+(1+x^2)xdy}{(1+x^2+y^2)^{3/2}}=0.$$

Since, in the above notation,

$$\frac{\partial P}{\partial y}=\frac{\partial}{\partial y}\left\{\frac{y+y^3}{(1+x^2+y^2)^{3/2}}\right\}=\frac{1+x^2+y^2+3x^2y^2}{(1+x^2+y^2)^{5/2}}$$

$$=\frac{\partial}{\partial x}\left\{\frac{x+x^3}{(1+x^2+y^2)^{3/2}}\right\}=\frac{\partial Q}{\partial x}$$

the equation is exact. Hence we are entitled to write

$$\begin{aligned}u(x, y)&=\int\frac{(1+y^2)ydx}{(1+x^2+y^2)^{3/2}}+\phi(y)\\&=\int\frac{ydx}{(1+x^2+y^2)^{1/2}}-\int\frac{x^2ydx}{(1+x^2+y^2)^{3/2}}+\phi(y)\\&=\int\frac{ydx}{(1+x^2+y^2)^{1/2}}+\int xy\frac{\partial}{\partial x}\left\{\frac{1}{(1+x^2+y^2)^{1/2}}\right\}dx+\phi(y)\\&=\frac{xy}{\sqrt{(1+x^2+y^2)}}+\phi(y),\end{aligned}$$

on integrating the second integral by parts. The equation

$$\frac{\partial u}{\partial y}=\frac{x+x^3}{(1+x^2+y^2)^{3/2}}+\phi'(y)$$

shows that $\phi'(y)$ is zero, or $\phi(y)$ is a constant. The general integral is therefore

$$\frac{xy}{\sqrt{(1+x^2+y^2)}}=C.$$

Note that although the given equation is exact as it stands, it would cease to be exact if the denominator of the left-hand member were removed.

Example 2.

$$\log(y^2+1)dx+\frac{2y(x-1)}{y^2+1}dy=0.$$

The condition for integrability is satisfied, therefore we write

$$\begin{aligned}u(x, y)&=\int\log(y^2+1)dx+\phi(y)\\&=x\log(y^2+1)+\phi(y).\end{aligned}$$

From this we obtain

$$\frac{\partial u}{\partial y}=\frac{2xy}{y^2+1}+\phi'(y);$$

comparison with the coefficient of dy in the given equation shows that

$$\phi'(y)=-\frac{2y}{y^2+1} \quad \text{or} \quad \phi(y)=-\log(y^2+1)+\text{const.}$$

The general integral therefore is

$$(x-1)\log(y^2+1)=C.$$

7. Integrating Factors. It will now be supposed that the condition for integrability (6.6) is not satisfied. This being so, an explicit general integral $u(x, y)=C$ is not immediately obtainable, but, on the other hand, the theory of the existence of integrals is able to establish the fact that a general integral in which the constant C is implicit does exist. This may be interpreted to mean that, given any non-exact equation

$$Pdx+Qdy=0, \quad . \quad . \quad . \quad (7.1)$$

there always exists an *integrating factor* $\mu(x, y)$ such that the modified equation

$$\mu Pdx+\mu Qdy=0 \quad . \quad . \quad . \quad (7.2)$$

is exact. Assuming that this is so, $\mu(x, y)$ must satisfy identically the relation

$$\frac{\partial(\mu P)}{\partial y}=\frac{\partial(\mu Q)}{\partial x} \quad . \quad . \quad . \quad (7.3)$$

or

$$P\frac{\partial\mu}{\partial y}-Q\frac{\partial\mu}{\partial x}+\mu\left\{\frac{\partial P}{\partial y}-\frac{\partial Q}{\partial x}\right\}=0. \quad . \quad . \quad (7.4)$$

To find a general solution of this *partial* differential equation is a vastly more advanced problem than that of solving the *ordinary* differential equation originally proposed. For present purposes, however, any particular solution of (7.4) would suffice, and such a solution may frequently be obtained by trial. When any integrating factor μ, satisfying (7.4), has been obtained and introduced into (7.2), this equation becomes exact and may be integrated by the method of § 6. The limitations of this method of integration are obvious; nevertheless there are particular cases which may be treated systematically; these will be indicated in § 9.

Example 1. The equation

$$ydx - xdy = 0$$

is not exact. Any integrating factor μ will satisfy

$$\frac{\partial(y\mu)}{\partial y} = -\frac{\partial(x\mu)}{\partial x}$$

or

$$x\frac{\partial\mu}{\partial x} + y\frac{\partial\mu}{\partial y} + 2\mu = 0.$$

It can be verified that

$$\frac{1}{x^2}, \quad \frac{1}{y^2}, \quad \frac{1}{xy}$$

are among the possible values of μ. Taking $\mu = 1/x^2$ we have

$$\frac{y}{x^2}dx - \frac{1}{x}dy = 0$$

which is exact and has the solution $y/x = C$. Similarly $\mu = 1/y^2$ leads to the equivalent solution $x/y = C'$. Taking $\mu = 1/xy$ we separate the variables:

$$\frac{dx}{x} - \frac{dy}{y} = 0$$

or

$$\log |x| - \log |y| = \text{const., whence } x/y = \text{const.}$$

Example 2.

$(1 + x^2 + y^2)^{-3/2}$ is an integrating factor for

$$(1 + y^2)ydx + (1 + x^2)xdy = 0. \qquad (\S\ 6,\ \text{Ex. } 1.)$$

Another integrating factor is the reciprocal of $xy(1 + x^2)(1 + y^2)$; this separates the variables.

8. The Quotient of Two Integrating Factors. Let μ_1 and μ_2 be two integrating factors of

$$Pdx+Qdy=0, \qquad (8.1)$$

whose ratio is not of itself a constant. Then the equation

$$\mu_2/\mu_1=C \quad \text{or} \quad \mu_2=C\mu_1 \qquad (8.2)$$

is an integral of (8.1). For (8.2) is a primitive of the differential equation

$$\left\{\mu_2\frac{\partial\mu_1}{\partial x}-\mu_1\frac{\partial\mu_2}{\partial x}\right\}dx+\left\{\mu_2\frac{\partial\mu_1}{\partial y}-\mu_1\frac{\partial\mu_2}{\partial y}\right\}dy=0. \qquad (8.3)$$

But since μ_1 and μ_2 are integrating factors of (8.1)

$$P\frac{\partial\mu_1}{\partial y}-Q\frac{\partial\mu_1}{\partial x}+\mu_1\left\{\frac{\partial P}{\partial y}-\frac{\partial Q}{\partial x}\right\}=0, \qquad (8.4)$$

$$P\frac{\partial\mu_2}{\partial y}-Q\frac{\partial\mu_2}{\partial x}+\mu_2\left\{\frac{\partial P}{\partial y}-\frac{\partial Q}{\partial x}\right\}=0, \qquad (8.5)$$

and hence

$$\mu_2\left\{P\frac{\partial\mu_1}{\partial y}-Q\frac{\partial\mu_1}{\partial x}\right\}-\mu_1\left\{P\frac{\partial\mu_2}{\partial y}-Q\frac{\partial\mu_2}{\partial x}\right\}=0,$$

i.e.

$$\left\{\mu_2\frac{\partial\mu_1}{\partial y}-\mu_1\frac{\partial\mu_2}{\partial y}\right\}P=\left\{\mu_2\frac{\partial\mu_1}{\partial x}-\mu_1\frac{\partial\mu_2}{\partial x}\right\}Q,$$

which reduces (8.3) to (8.1), thereby proving the theorem.

This theorem is equivalent to the statement that if one integrating factor of (8.1) is known, an unlimited number of others may be obtained. Thus if μ_1 is known and we write $\mu_2=v\mu_1$, we have from (8.5)

$$P\frac{\partial(v\mu_1)}{\partial y}-Q\frac{\partial(v\mu_1)}{\partial x}+v\mu_1\left\{\frac{\partial P}{\partial y}-\frac{\partial Q}{\partial x}\right\}=0$$

which, on account of (8.4), reduces to

$$\mu_1\left\{P\frac{\partial v}{\partial y}-Q\frac{\partial v}{\partial x}\right\}=0$$

so that $v=$const. is any general integral of (8.1). But if $u=C$ is one form of this general integral, we have $v=F(u)$.

Thus

$$\mu_2 = \mu_1 F(u),$$

where $F(u)$ is any arbitrary function of u.

Example. Referring to § 7, Ex. 1, we see that solutions of the equation are

$$\frac{1}{x^2} \div \frac{1}{y^2} = \text{const.}, \qquad \frac{1}{x^2} \div \frac{1}{xy} = \text{const.}, \qquad \frac{1}{y^2} \div \frac{1}{xy} = \text{const.},$$

all of which are equivalent to $y/x = C$. Furthermore, an infinite number of integrating factors is included in the formula

$$\mu = \frac{1}{xy} F\left(\frac{y}{x}\right).$$

9. Special Types of Integrating Factor. It may happen that an integrating factor can be found which depends on one variable only. Consider, for example, the circumstances in which

$$Pdx + Qdy = 0$$

admits of an integrating factor $\mu(x)$ depending upon x alone. That being the case, (7.4) will become

$$Q\frac{d\mu}{dx} = \mu\left\{\frac{\partial P}{\partial y} - \frac{\partial Q}{\partial x}\right\}$$

or

$$\frac{d\mu}{dx} \Big/ \mu = \left\{\frac{\partial P}{\partial y} - \frac{\partial Q}{\partial x}\right\} \Big/ Q. \qquad (9.1)$$

Thus μ can be a function of x alone if the right-hand member of this equation is independent of y; μ is then determined by a quadrature.

Example.

$$(1 - xy)dx + (xy - x^2)dy = 0.$$

In the above notation,

$$\left(\frac{\partial P}{\partial y} - \frac{\partial Q}{\partial x}\right) \Big/ Q = \frac{-x - (y - 2x)}{xy - x^2} = -\frac{1}{x}.$$

Hence

$$\frac{d\mu}{\mu} = -\frac{dx}{x}, \qquad \log|\mu| = -\log|x| \quad \text{or} \quad \mu = \frac{1}{x}.$$

With this factor introduced, the equation becomes

$$\left(\frac{1}{x} - y\right)dx + (y - x)dy = 0;$$

it is now exact and has the integral

$$\log|x| - xy + \tfrac{1}{2}y^2 = C.$$

In the same way, assuming the existence of an integrating factor which is a function of $x+y$, say

$$\mu = f(x+y) = f(z),$$

it will be found that

$$\frac{f'(z)}{f(z)} = -\left\{\frac{\partial P}{\partial y} - \frac{\partial Q}{\partial x}\right\}\Big/(P - Q). \quad . \quad . \quad (9.2)$$

Therefore a necessary condition for the existence of such an integrating factor is that the right-hand member of (9.2) shall be a function of z, or $x+y$, alone; μ is then determined by a quadrature.

Example.

$$(5x^2 + 2xy + 3y^3)dx + 3(x^2 + xy^2 + 2y^3)dy = 0.$$

Condition (9.2) here becomes

$$\frac{f'(z)}{f(z)} = -\frac{6y^2 - 4x}{2x^2 + 2xy - 3xy^2 - 3y^3} = \frac{2}{x+y} = \frac{2}{z}$$

and therefore the condition is satisfied. We have $f(z) = z^2$ and therefore the integrating factor is $(x+y)^2$. Introducing it and integrating, we obtain the general integral

$$(x^2 + y^3)(x+y)^3 = C.$$

Again, if it is assumed that

$$\mu = f(xy) = f(z)$$

the condition will become

$$\frac{f'(z)}{f(z)} = -\left\{\frac{\partial P}{\partial y} - \frac{\partial Q}{\partial x}\right\}\Big/(Px - Qy), \quad . \quad . \quad (9.3)$$

where the right-hand member must be a function of z, or xy, alone; here again μ is determined by a quadrature.

Example.

$$(xy^3 + 2x^2y^2 - y^2)dx + (x^2y^2 + 2x^3y - 2x^2)dy = 0.$$

Condition (9.3) becomes

$$\frac{f'(z)}{f(z)} = \frac{xy^2 - 2x^2y - 2y + 4x}{xy^2 - 2x^2y} = 1 - \frac{2}{xy} = 1 - \frac{2}{z}$$

whence $f(z) = e^z z^{-2}$. An integrating factor is therefore $\mu = e^{xy}x^{-2}y^{-2}$; it leads to the general integral

$$e^{xy}\left(\frac{1}{x} + \frac{2}{y}\right) = C.$$

10. The Linear Equation. An equation of the type

$$f(x)y' + g(x)y = h(x),$$

which involves y and y' linearly, is said to be linear. By dividing throughout by $f(x)$ it may be brought into the standard form

$$y' + py = q, \quad . \quad . \quad . \quad (10.1)$$

where p and q are functions of x alone. When condition (9.1) is applied to the equivalent differential form

$$dy + (py - q)dx = 0$$

it reveals the existence of an integrating factor which is a function of x alone. In fact, if the factor $\mu(x)$ is introduced the condition of integrability reduces to

$$\frac{d\mu}{dx} = \frac{\partial(\mu py - \mu q)}{\partial y} = \mu p$$

or

$$d\mu/\mu = pdx. \quad . \quad . \quad . \quad (10.2)$$

Integrating,

$$\log \mu = \int pdx, \quad \text{whence} \quad \mu = e^{\int pdx}.$$

The exact equation

$$e^{\int pdx}dy + (py - q)e^{\int pdx}dx = 0$$

has the general integral

$$ye^{\int pdx} - \int qe^{\int pdx}dx = C, \quad . \quad . \quad . \quad (10.3)$$

which thus involves two quadratures.

Note 1. When the integrating factor μ has been obtained and introduced, the equation may be written

$$\mu dy + \mu' y dx = q\mu dx \qquad (\text{for } \mu p = \mu')$$

or

$$d(\mu y) = q\mu dx,$$

and integrating,

$$\mu y = \int q\mu dx + C.$$

The general integral is therefore of the form

$$y = C\mu^{-1} + \mu^{-1}\int q\mu dx. \quad . \quad . \quad . \quad (10.4)$$

Note 2. Replacing q by zero in (10.1) we obtain the corresponding *reduced* equation, homogeneous in y and y':

$$y' + py = 0; \quad . \quad . \quad . \quad (10.5)$$

its general integral involves only one quadrature:

$$y = Ce^{-\int pdx}.$$

Note 3. If any particular solution of (10.1), say $y = y_1$, is known, the general integral is obtainable by a quadrature. For we then have

$$y_1' + py_1 = q,$$

and eliminating q between this equation and (10.1); also writing v for $y - y_1$, we have

$$v' + pv = 0,$$

i.e. the corresponding reduced equation. Thus the general integral of (10.1) is

$$\begin{aligned} y &= v + y_1 \\ &= Ce^{-\int pdx} + y_1. \quad . \quad . \quad . \quad (10.6) \end{aligned}$$

It consists of two terms: the first is taken from the general integral of the reduced equation and is known as the *complementary function*, the second is any particular integral.

Note 4. The difference between any two particular integrals is a special case of the complementary function.

For since the relation

$$y - y_1 = Ce^{-\int p dx}$$

is general, any particular integral y_2 is obtained by attributing the appropriate value to C, say C':

$$y_2 - y_1 = C'e^{-\int p dx}.$$

Note 5. If y_1 and y_2 are any two particular integrals,

$$\frac{y - y_1}{y_2 - y_1} = \text{const.} \quad . \quad . \quad . \quad (10.7)$$

furnishes the general integral.

Example.

$$xy' - (x+1)y = x^2 - x^3.$$

Dividing by the coefficient of y' we reduce the equation to the standard form

$$y' - \frac{x+1}{x}y = x - x^2.$$

If μ is the integrating factor,

$$\log \mu = -\int \frac{x+1}{x} dx = -x - \log x$$

or

$$\mu = e^{-x}/x.$$

Introducing μ into the equation in its standard (not its original) form, we have

$$\frac{e^{-x}y'}{x} - \frac{x+1}{x^2}e^{-x}y = e^{-x}(1-x)$$

or

$$\frac{d}{dx}\left(\frac{e^{-x}y}{x}\right) = e^{-x}(1-x),$$

i.e.

$$e^{-x}y/x = C + \int e^{-x}(1-x)dx = C + xe^{-x},$$

so that the general integral is

$$y = Cxe^x + x^2.$$

Application. A condenser of capacity C (farads) is being charged from a source of electricity of potential E (volts) through a non-inductive resistance R (ohms). The charge Q (coulombs) at time t (seconds) is given by the linear differential equation

$$R\frac{dQ}{dt}+\frac{Q}{C}=E.$$

If the initial charge is zero, it is required to find Q at any instant (i) when the voltage E is constant; (ii) when the voltage is alternating, *i.e.* $E=E_0 \sin pt$, where E_0 and p are constants.

Following the general method of integration we find that, whatever E may be,

$$Qe^{t/RC}=K+\int\frac{E}{R}e^{t/RC}dt,$$

where K is the constant of integration.

(i) When E is constant,

$$Qe^{t/RC}=K+CEe^{t/RC}.$$

The constant K is determined by the *initial condition* that $Q=0$ when $t=0$, so that

$$0=K+CE,$$

i.e.

$$Qe^{t/RC}=CE(e^{t/RC}-1).$$

Thus the charge at time t is given by

$$Q=CE(1-e^{-t/RC}),$$

which approximates to the steady value CE when t is large.

(ii) When $E=E_0 \sin pt$,

$$e^{t/RC}Q=K+\frac{E_0}{R}\int e^{t/RC}\sin pt\,dt$$

$$=K+CE_0e^{t/RC}(\sin pt-RCp\cos pt)/(1+R^2C^2p^2).$$

Since $Q=0$ when $t=0$ we have

$$0=K-RC^2pE_0/(1+R^2C^2p^2)$$

and hence

$$Q=\frac{CE_0}{1+R^2C^2p^2}(\sin pt-RCp\cos pt+RCpe^{-t/RC}).$$

The influence of the exponential term diminishes rapidly, so that Q approximates to a form of the same period as E.

C

11. The Bernoulli Equation. The equation

$$y' + py = qy^n \quad . \quad . \quad . \quad (11.1)$$

in which p and q are functions of x alone, is associated with the name of James Bernoulli. It may be reduced to linear form by a change in the dependent variable. For the result of division throughout by y^n:

$$y^{-n}y' + py^{1-n} = q$$

suggests the substitution

$$v = y^{1-n}, \qquad v' = (1-n)y^{-n}y'.$$

The equation then becomes

$$v' + (1-n)pv = (1-n)q, \quad . \quad . \quad (11.2)$$

which is of the standard linear type in v.

Example.

$$\frac{dy}{dx} - \frac{y}{2x} = 5x^2y^5.$$

The above steps give, in turn:

$$\frac{y'}{y^5} - \frac{1}{2xy^4} = 5x^2$$

$$v = y^{-4}, \qquad v' = -4y^{-5}y'$$

$$v' + \frac{2}{x}v = -20x^2.$$

This linear equation has the integrating factor x^2:

$$x^2v' + 2xv = -20x^4.$$

Integrating:

$$x^2v = C - 4x^5 \quad \text{or} \quad v = Cx^{-2} - 4x^3$$

and since $y = v^{-1/4}$,

$$y = \frac{1}{\sqrt[4]{(Cx^{-2} - 4x^3)}}.$$

12. The Riccati Equation. The standard form of this equation is

$$y' = py^2 + qy + r, \quad . \quad . \quad . \quad (12.1)$$

where p, q, r are functions of x alone, and p is not identically zero. It may be integrated completely when any particular solution, say $y=y_1$, is known, a result which is achieved by the substitution

$$y=y_1+1/v,$$

where v is a new dependent variable. After simplification it will be found that the equation in v is linear, namely:

$$v'+(2py_1+q)v+p=0 \quad . \quad . \quad (12.2)$$

and the integration can be completed by quadratures.

Note 1. The general integral may be expressed directly in terms of any three functions y_1, y_2, y_3 which satisfy the equation. For if we make the substitution $y=y_1+1/v$, y_2 and y_3 will correspond to two particular values of v, say v_1 and v_2, thus:

$$y_2=y_1+1/v_1, \qquad y_3=y_1+1/v_2,$$

and since $v=v_1$ and $v=v_2$ are particular solutions of the linear equation (12.2) its general solution will be (10.7)

$$\frac{v-v_1}{v_2-v_1}=C.$$

Making the reverse substitutions

$$v=\frac{1}{y-y_1}, \qquad v_1=\frac{1}{y_2-y_1}, \qquad v_2=\frac{1}{y_3-y_1}$$

we find that

$$\frac{y-y_2}{y-y_1}=C\frac{y_3-y_2}{y_3-y_1}$$

which furnishes the general integral.

Note 2. If $y=y_4$ is a fourth particular solution, we have

$$\frac{y_4-y_2}{y_4-y_1}\cdot\frac{y_3-y_1}{y_3-y_2}=C,$$

i.e. the cross-ratio of any four solutions is a constant.

Example.

$$2x^2y'=(x-1)(y^2-x^2)+2xy.$$

The solutions $y=x$, $y=-x$ are evident on inspection. Taking the former, we write

$$y=x+1/v, \qquad y'=1-v'/v^2$$

and derive the linear equation

$$2x^2(v'+v)=1-x;$$

its general integral is

$$v=(Cxe^{-x}-1)/2x.$$

The general integral of the proposed equation is therefore

$$y=x+\frac{2x}{Cxe^{-x}-1}=x\frac{Cxe^{-x}+1}{Cxe^{-x}-1}=x\frac{Cx+e^x}{Cx-e^x}.$$

The cross-ratio of the four particular functions x, $-x$, $x\dfrac{x+e^x}{x-e^x}$, $x\dfrac{x-e^x}{x+e^x}$ which satisfy the equation will be found to be -1.

13. Change of Variable. To sum up, equations which may be readily integrated by quadratures are those with separable variables, those of the homogeneous type, exact and linear equations. In the homogeneous type, the variables are made separable by the substitution $v=y/x$ by which a change of dependent variable is effected. Actually the method of integrating an equation with separable variables, or a linear equation, is to introduce an integrating factor which renders it exact; this is the fundamental principle upon which integration of equations of the first order and degree essentially depends. If other equations can be integrated it is because a change in variable (as in the case of the Bernoulli equation) has enabled a reduction to one of the above types to be performed.

When an equation is proposed for solution and does not appear to come under one or other of the foregoing headings, it is advisable to consider if a change in one or both of the variables cannot be discovered which will transform the equation into one of a recognisable type, just as a change in the dependent variable of a Bernoulli equation rendered it linear.

For instance, if an equation is of the form

$$\frac{dy}{dx}=f(ax+by+c),$$

the substitution $v=ax+by$ at once suggests itself. It transforms the equation into

$$\frac{dv}{dx}=a+bf(v+c),$$

where the variables are separable.

Again, an equation such as

$$\{xf(y)+g(y)\}\frac{dy}{dx}=h(y)$$

may not be integrable as it stands, but if y is taken as the independent and x as the dependent variable, it may be written

$$h(y)\frac{dx}{dy}-f(y)x=g(y),$$

when it becomes a linear equation in x.

It is not possible, even if it were desirable, to formulate a set of rules governing changes of variable, but one or two combinations of symbols frequently occur and deserve special mention. Thus if the differential $xdx+ydy$ is a component part of the equation, it naturally suggests $u=x^2+y^2$ as a new variable; if $xdy-ydx$ occurs it suggests $v=x/y$ or $v=y/x$. When both $xdx+ydy$ and $xdy-ydx$ are present, simplification is very often obtained by a change to polar co-ordinates through the substitutions

$$x=r\cos\theta, \qquad y=r\sin\theta,$$

$$xdx+ydy=rdr, \qquad xdy-ydx=r^2d\theta.$$

In this case it is usually best to leave the general integral expressed in terms of r, θ.

Example 1.

$$(xy+1)dx+2x^2(2xy-1)dy=0.$$

The prominence of xy in the equation suggests that $v=xy$ might be taken as a new variable in place of y. The equation then becomes

$$(4v^2-3v-1)dx-2x(2v-1)dv=0.$$

The variables are separable; the usual process of integration leads to the general integral

$$(4xy+1)^3(xy-1)^2=Cx^5.$$

Example 2. An equation of the type

$$xy'-y=f(x)g(y/x)$$

is transformed by the substitution $y=vx$ into

$$x^2v'=f(x)g(v),$$

whose variables are separable. For instance,

$$xy'-y=2x\frac{y^2-x^2}{x^4-1}$$

becomes, after transformation and separation,

$$\frac{dv}{v^2-1}=\frac{2xdx}{x^4-1},$$

whence

$$\frac{v-1}{v+1}=C\frac{x^2-1}{x^2+1}.$$

If $c=(1-C)/(1+C)$, the general integral is

$$y=x\frac{x^2+c}{cx^2+1}.$$

Example 3.

$$(x^2+y^2)(xdx+ydy)+(x^2+y^2-2x+2y)(ydx-xdy)=0.$$

Changing to polar co-ordinates, we obtain, cancelling r^2,

$$dr-(r-2\cos\theta+2\sin\theta)d\theta=0.$$

This is linear in r and has the general integral

$$r=Ce^{\theta}-2\sin\theta.$$

CHAPTER II

INTEGRAL CURVES

14. Families of Plane Curves. When referred to rectangular axes of co-ordinates, the equation $f(x, y)=C$ represents, for any definite value of the *parameter* C, a plane curve. The aggregate of all values of C for which the equation is possible gives a complete *one-parameter family* of curves. Thus the equation $x^2+y^2=C$, wherein all positive values are in turn assigned to C, represents the family of all circles whose centres are at the origin.

The corresponding differential equation

$$P(x, y)dx+Q(x, y)dy=0 \quad . \quad . \quad (14.1)$$

does not involve the parameter C; it is therefore representative of some geometrical property or other that is common to all members of the family of curves. Any pair of values (x, y) for which P and Q have definite real values corresponds to a point in the plane at which the value of the gradient $y'=dy/dx$ can be evaluated by means of (14.1). The only exception to this statement arises when the ratio P/Q becomes indeterminate, a case that will be investigated later.

Thus the integration of the differential equation (14.1) is equivalent to the geometrical problem of discovering the family of plane curves, *the integral curves*, such that the gradient at any point (x, y) is an assigned function of the pair of variables (x, y). If P and Q are one-valued, then there will be one value of y', and only one, corresponding to any point for which the ratio P/Q is determinate.

This amounts to the statement that *through any point (x, y) in general there passes but one integral curve of a differential equation of the first order and degree.*

The symbolic expression of any geometrical problem that involves, directly or indirectly, the gradient at any point is in fact a differential equation of the first order. It may, however, be of higher degree than the first, but for the moment problems that lead to equations of the first order and degree will suffice as examples.

If P be any point (x, y) on a plane curve, let T, N, G be the points at which the tangent, ordinate and normal at P respectively meet the x-axis. Then if ψ is the angle between TP and the positive direction of the x-axis,

$$y' = \tan \psi.$$

The gradient may be introduced indirectly, *e.g.*

$$\text{Subnormal} = NG = NP \tan \psi = yy' = y\frac{dy}{dx}.$$

$$\text{Subtangent} = TN = NP \cot \psi = y/y' = y\frac{dx}{dy}.$$

The lengths PT, PG are known as the "tangent" and "normal" respectively; they involve y' but not linearly.

Example 1. Curves whose subnormal has the constant value $2a$:

$$yy' = 2a \quad \text{or} \quad ydy = 2adx.$$

Integrating:

$$y^2 = 4a(x + C)$$

which represents a family of equal parabolas, with axes coincident with the x-axis.

Example 2. Curves whose subtangent has the constant value a:

$$y\frac{dx}{dy} = a \quad \text{or} \quad \frac{dy}{y} = \frac{dx}{a}.$$

Integrating:

$$\log y = \log C + \frac{x}{a} \quad \text{or} \quad y = Ce^{x/a},$$

a family of exponential curves.

Example 3. Curves in which the subtangent is twice the abscissa:

$$y\frac{dx}{dy} = 2x.$$

The variables are separable: the integral curves are the family of parabolas $y^2 = Cx$.

Example 4. The ordinate at any point is equal to the perpendicular from the origin to the normal at that point.

If (X, Y) is any point on the normal at (x, y),

$$X + Yy' = x + yy'$$

and therefore the length of the perpendicular from the origin is

$$\frac{x + yy'}{\sqrt{(1 + y'^2)}} = y.$$

This symbolic statement involves y'^2 as it stands, but on rationalisation and simplification it reduces to an equation of the first degree in y':

$$x^2 + 2xyy' = y^2$$

or

$$2xydy + (x^2 - y^2)dx = 0.$$

This can be integrated as an equation of homogeneous type (§ 4, Ex. 1) or as one which has for an integrating factor a function of x alone. The second method is the simpler; the integrating factor x^{-2} leads to the general integral

$$x^2 + y^2 = Cx,$$

representing a family of circles touching the y-axis at the origin.

15. Trajectories. Let

$$f(x, y, \alpha) = 0 \quad \text{and} \quad g(x, y, \beta) = 0$$

be the equations of two families of curves each dependent

upon one parameter. When each member of the family β cuts every member of the family α according to a definite law, any curve of either of the families is said to be a *trajectory* of the other family. The most important case is that in which curves of the families intersect at a constant angle.

When a curve intersects all the members of a family of curves at right angles, it is said to be an *orthogonal trajectory* of that family. Thus any circle of centre O is the orthogonal trajectory of the family of straight lines radiating from O, and conversely any line through O is the orthogonal trajectory of all circles concentric with O. That is, the families

$$x^2+y^2=a^2, \qquad y=\beta x$$

are mutually orthogonal.

In rectangular co-ordinates let

$$P(x, y)dx+Q(x, y)dy=0 \quad . \quad . \quad (15.1)$$

be the differential equation of one family of curves; when written in the form

$$y'=-P(x, y)/Q(x, y),$$

it expresses the fact that if an integral curve passes through (x, y) it will have a certain gradient at that point. The gradient of the orthogonal curve through that point will be the negative reciprocal, *i.e.*

$$y'=Q(x, y)/P(x, y).$$

In other words, an orthogonal trajectory will be an integral curve of the differential equation

$$P(x, y)dy-Q(x, y)dx=0. \quad . \quad . \quad (15.2)$$

Moreover, whenever an integral curve of (15.2) meets an integral curve of (15.1) it will cut it at right angles.

Thus the differential equation of the one family is obtained from that of the other by replacing dx by dy and dy by $-dx$, or, what is the same thing, by replacing

y' by $-1/y'$. *If the differential equation of the family* $f(x, y, a)=0$ *is* $F(x, y, y')=0$, *the differential equation of the orthogonal family will be* $F(x, y, -1/y')=0$, *and its general integral* $g(x, y, \beta)=0$ *will be the orthogonal family itself.*

When the curves of the families $f(x, y, a)=0$ and $g(x, y, \beta)=0$ intersect at a constant angle other than a right angle, the trajectories are said to be *oblique*. To make the problem definite, let the tangent at (x, y) to the curve of $f=0$ make the angle ψ with the x-axis; let the inclination of the tangent to $g=0$ at (x, y) be ψ_1 and let the law connecting them be $\psi_1=\psi+\omega$. Then

$$\tan\psi=\frac{\tan\psi_1-\tan\omega}{1+\tan\psi_1\tan\omega}=\frac{\tan\psi_1-m}{1+m\tan\psi_1},$$

writing m for $\tan\omega$.

Let the differential equation of the original family be

$$F(x, y, y')=0,$$

or since $y'=\tan\psi$ in the original family,

$$F(x, y, \tan\psi)=0,$$

or again

$$F\left(x, y, \frac{\tan\psi_1-m}{1+m\tan\psi_1}\right)=0.$$

But in the family of oblique trajectories $y'=\tan\psi_1$ and therefore this family consists of the integral curves of the differential equation

$$F\left(x, y, \frac{y'-m}{1+my'}\right)=0.$$

If therefore the differential equation of a family of plane curves is known, the differential equation of the family that intersects it at a positive angle ω is obtained by replacing y' wherever it occurs by $(y'-m)/(1+my')$, where $m=\tan\omega$, or, what is the same thing, by replacing dy by $dy-mdx$ and also dx by $dx+mdy$.

Let $f(r, \theta, a)$ represent a one-parameter family of plane curves in polar co-ordinates, and let the differential equation of the family be $F(r, \theta, dr/d\theta)=0$. Let (r, θ) be any point through which a curve passes, and let ϕ be the angle which the tangent at that point makes with the radius vector, so that

$$\tan\phi = r\frac{d\theta}{dr}.$$

An oblique trajectory, of angle ω, will be such that the angle which its tangent makes with the radius vector will be $\phi_1 = \phi + \omega$, and we have

$$\begin{aligned}\tan\phi &= \tan(\phi_1 - \omega)\\ &= \frac{\tan\phi_1 - \tan\omega}{1+\tan\phi_1\tan\omega} = \frac{rd\theta/dr - m}{1+mrd\theta/dr} = \frac{rd\theta - mdr}{dr + mrd\theta}.\end{aligned}$$

Thus the differential equation of the oblique trajectories will be obtained from that of the original family by replacing $rd\theta$ by $rd\theta - mdr$ and dr by $dr + mrd\theta$.

In the case of orthogonal trajectories we should have $\phi_1 = \phi \pm \frac{1}{2}\pi$ or

$$\tan\phi_1 = -\cot\phi = -\frac{1}{r}\frac{dr}{d\theta}$$

so that $rd\theta$ is replaced by $-dr$ and dr by $rd\theta$.

Example 1. The equation

$$x^2 + y^2 - 2ax = 0$$

represents, for varying a, all circles which touch the y-axis at the origin, the centre of any individual circle being $(a, 0)$. Its differential equation (§ 14, Ex. 4) is

$$(x^2 - y^2)dx + 2xydy = 0.$$

To find the equation of the orthogonal trajectories replace dx by dy, dy by $-dx$:

$$(x^2 - y^2)dy - 2xydx = 0,$$

which is really the same equation with x and y interchanged throughout. Its general integral therefore is

$$x^2 + y^2 - 2\beta y = 0,$$

so that the orthogonal trajectories are all circles which touch the x-axis at the origin.

Example 2. It may happen that any one member of a family intersects at right angles an infinite set (not necessarily all) of members of the same set. Such a family is said to be *self-orthogonal*.* For example, consider the family of confocal parabolas

$$y^2 = 4c(x + c),$$

i.e. parabolas with a common focus at the origin and common axis Ox.

We have

$$y\frac{dy}{dx} = 2c$$

and eliminating c,

$$y = 2x\frac{dy}{dx} + y\left(\frac{dy}{dx}\right)^2$$

or

$$y(dy^2 - dx^2) + 2xdxdy = 0.$$

This, the differential equation of the family of parabolas, remains essentially unaltered if dy is replaced by $-dx$ and dx by dy, so that the family is, in fact, self-orthogonal. To see how this property originates, consider the two particular curves

$$y^2 = 4a(x + a), \qquad y^2 = 4b(x + b).$$

Their point of intersection has the abscissa $x = -(a + b)$ and the ordinate is given by $y^2 = -4ab$. Thus the intersection is real only when a and b are of opposite signs. When that is the case, the gradients of the two curves at the point of intersection are respectively either $\sqrt{(-a/b)}$ and $-\sqrt{(-b/a)}$ or $-\sqrt{(-a/b)}$ and $\sqrt{(-b/a)}$, which verifies their orthogonality.

Example 3. To find the oblique trajectories of the family of straight lines

$$y = ax.$$

* This cannot happen if the differential equation of the family is of the first degree in y'; the example given leads to an equation of the second degree.

The differential equation of the family is $xy' = y$ or

$$xdy = ydx,$$

and therefore that of the trajectories:

$$x(dy - mdx) = y(dx + mdy)$$

or

$$xdy - ydx = m(xdx + ydy).$$

Clearly this is a case for a change to polar co-ordinates, which gives

$$rd\theta = mdr.$$

The general integral is $r = \beta e^{\theta/m}$, *i.e.* the trajectories consist of a family of equiangular spirals.

Example 4. In polar co-ordinates the family of circles given in Ex. 1 is

$$r = 2a \cos \theta,$$

and its differential equation is

$$dr = -r \tan \theta \, d\theta.$$

The orthogonal trajectories, which are the integral curves of

$$rd\theta = \tan \theta \, dr,$$

are the family

$$r = 2\beta \sin \theta.$$

16. Level Lines and Lines of Slope on a Surface. Let the surface be referred to a rectangular system of axes with the z-axis vertical; the (x, y)-plane will be the horizontal reference plane. The section made on the surface by a horizontal plane $z = a$ is a *level line* or *contour line* of level a. The horizontal projections of the various level lines made by a regular sequence of horizontal planes $z = a_1$, a_2, . . . form a *contour map*. If a is varied continuously, as it does when the secant plane moves uniformly upwards, the contour map is replaced by a family of curves in the (x, y)-plane dependent upon the parameter a. If the equation of the surface is $f(x, y, z) = 0$ these curves will be contained in the equation $f(x, y, a) = 0$.

The *lines of steepest slope* on the surface are the lines

of minimum distance between successive contours, and are therefore lines cutting the level lines at right angles. On account of the fact that when two curves in space, one of which lies in a horizontal plane, cut orthogonally, their horizontal projections will cut orthogonally, we see that on the horizontal reference plane, the projections of the lines of steepest slope are the orthogonal trajectories of the contour lines. If the equation of these trajectories is $g(x, y, \beta)=0$, the lines of steepest slope on the surface will be the intersections of the surface by the cylinders $g(x, y, \beta)=0$ whose generators are parallel to the z-axis.

Example. Consider the paraboloid

$$2z=ax^2+by^2.$$

The level lines project into the family of curves

$$ax^2+by^2=2a,$$

whose differential equation is

$$axdx+bydy=0.$$

The orthogonal trajectories, whose differential equation is

$$axdy-bydx=0,$$

will be found to be $y^a=\beta x^b$, and hence the lines of steepest slope may be found.

In particular, when $a=b$, *i.e.* in the case of a paraboloid of revolution, the lines of steepest slope are the intersections of the surface by all planes through the z-axis; that is, they are meridian lines on the surface.

17. Singular Points. Let (x_0, y_0) be a point such that, in its neighbourhood, the functions $P(x, y)$, $Q(x, y)$ are finite, continuous and single-valued. Then the equation

$$P(x, y)dx+Q(x, y)dy=0 \qquad . \quad . \quad (17.1)$$

assigns the value $y'=-P(x_0, y_0)/Q(x_0, y_0)$ to the gradient at that point, and this value is determinate with the sole exception of the case

$$P(x_0, y_0)=0, \qquad Q(x_0, y_0)=0. \quad . \quad . \quad (17.2)$$

Points at which the gradient becomes indeterminate through the simultaneous vanishing of P and Q are said to be *singular*. Thus singular points are the points of intersection of the curves $P(x, y)=0$ and $Q(x, y)=0$, which are the loci of points at which the integral curves have tangents parallel to the x-axis and the y-axis respectively.* They are thus, in general, isolated points.

To illustrate possible modes of behaviour of the integral curves in the neighbourhood of a singular point, we shall consider the *linear fractional equation*

$$\frac{dy}{dx}=\frac{ax+by}{lx+my} \quad (am-bl\neq 0). \qquad . \quad (17.3)$$

for which the origin is the only finite singular point.

Making the usual substitution $y=vx$, we obtain

$$x\frac{dv}{dx}=\frac{a+(b-l)v-mv^2}{l+mv}. \qquad . \qquad . \quad (17.4)$$

If $v-\alpha$, $v-\beta$ are factors of the numerator, $v=\alpha$, $v=\beta$ will be particular solutions of (17.4), and $y=\alpha x$, $y=\beta x$ of (17.3) Thus among the integral curves of (17.3) are two straight lines through the origin, whose joint equation is

$$ax^2+(b-l)xy-my^2=0.$$

These are known as the *principal lines*, and α, β the *principal directions* through the origin. They are real and distinct, coincident, or imaginary according as

$$(b-l)^2+4am >, \ = \text{ or } < 0.$$

When they are real, (17.4) may be written

$$x\frac{dv}{dx}+\frac{m(v-\alpha)(v-\beta)}{l+mv}=0.$$

* It is assumed that $P=0$ and $Q=0$ have not a branch in common. If $R=0$ were a branch common to both, R could be cancelled out of the equation, and the above statement would be strictly true.

Separating the variables and integrating, we obtain

$$\log |x| + \mu \log |v - a| + \nu \log |v - \beta| = \log C$$

or

$$x(v-a)^{\mu}(v-\beta)^{\nu} = C,$$

where

$$\mu = \frac{l + ma}{m(a-\beta)}, \qquad \nu = \frac{l + m\beta}{m(\beta - a)}, \qquad \mu + \nu = 1,$$

and thus the general integral of (17.3), when the principal directions are real and distinct, is

$$(y - ax)^{\mu}(y - \beta x)^{\nu} = C.$$

When μ and ν are both positive, this represents a family of curves having asymptotes $y = ax$, $y = \beta x$ in common. The asymptotes themselves are integral curves, but apart from them, no integral curves pass through the origin, which is a *col* of the family.* When μ and ν are of opposite signs, the equation of the integral curves may be written

$$y - \beta x = c(y - ax)^{\rho}, \qquad \text{where } \rho = -\mu/\nu.$$

Since ρ is positive, every integral curve passes through the origin, which is a *base point* or *nodal point* of the family. When $\rho = 1$, *i.e.* $\mu = -\nu$, the integral curves pass through the origin in all directions; the nodal point is then said to be *isotropic*. When $\rho > 1$, *i.e.* $|\mu| > |\nu|$, $y = ax$ and $y = \beta x$ are integral curves; all other integral curves touch the principal line $y = \beta x$ at the origin. When $0 < \rho < 1$, *i.e.* $|\mu| < |\nu|$, $y = ax$ and $y = \beta x$ are integral curves; all other integral curves touch $y = ax$ at the origin.

When the principal directions coincide with that of the line $y = ax$, (17.4) may be written

$$x\frac{dv}{dx} + \frac{m(v-a)^2}{l + mv} = 0,$$

* The origin is a saddle-point on the surface $z = (y - ax)^{\mu}(y - \beta x)^{\nu}$.

whence

$$\log|x| + \log|v - a| - \frac{l + ma}{m(v - a)} = C,$$

and thus the general integral of (17.3) is

$$(y - ax)(\log|y - ax| - C) = (l/m + a)x,$$

from which we derive

$$y' = a + \frac{l/m + a}{1 - C + \log|y - ax|}.$$

Thus the line $y = ax$, which is itself an integral curve, is tangential at the origin to every other integral curve.

When the principal directions are imaginary, we may write $a = \kappa + i\lambda$, $\beta = \kappa - i\lambda$, whereupon (17.4) becomes

$$x\frac{dv}{dx} + \frac{m\{(v - \kappa)^2 + \lambda^2\}}{l + mv} = 0.$$

Separating the variables and integrating, we have

$$\log|x| + \tfrac{1}{2}\log\{(v - \kappa)^2 + \lambda^2\} + \frac{l + m\kappa}{m\lambda}\arctan\frac{v - \kappa}{\lambda} = \log C,$$

and hence the general integral of (17.3) is

$$\tfrac{1}{2}\log\{(y - \kappa x)^2 + \lambda^2 x^2\} + \frac{l + m\kappa}{m\lambda}\arctan\frac{y - \kappa x}{\lambda x} = \log C.$$

If $l + m\kappa = 0$, the integral curves

$$(y - \kappa x)^2 + \lambda^2 x^2 = C^2$$

are a family of ellipses encircling the singular point at the origin, which is their *centre* and *limiting point*. In the general case we make the substitution *

$$y - \kappa x = r\sin\theta, \qquad \lambda x = r\cos\theta$$

and obtain

$$\log r + \mu\theta = \log C, \quad \text{where} \quad \mu = (l + m\kappa)/m\lambda,$$

or

$$r = Ce^{-\mu\theta}.$$

* This transformation may be regarded as a strain $\eta = y - \kappa x$, $\xi = \lambda x$ consisting of a shear in the direction of the y-axis and an extension in the direction of the x-axis, followed by a change to polar co-ordinates.

This is the equation of an equiangular spiral which winds asymptotically round the origin. The transformation back to the x, y-plane involves no deformation other than a simple strain, so that the integral curves are in general spirals with a common *asymptotic point* at the origin.

Note. When (17.1) has a singular point at the origin it may be written

$$\frac{dy}{dx}=\frac{ax+by+p(x, y)}{lx+my+q(x, y)},$$

where $p(x, y)$, $q(x, y)$ can be developed as series whose lowest terms are of the second degree at least. It can be shown that unless $a=b=0$ or $l=m=0$ the integral curves behave, in the neighbourhood of the origin, as if p and q were absent, and precisely the same cases arise.

Example 1.

$$\frac{dy}{dx}=\frac{my-x^n}{x} \qquad (n\neq m,\ n>1).$$

The general integral $y=Cx^m-x^n/(n-m)$ shows that y is of the order of x^m or x^n according as $m<$ or $>n$. When $m<0$, the origin is a *col* of the integral curves ; when $m>0$, it is a *nodal point*, with integral curves touching the y-axis when $m<1$, and the x-axis when $m>1$.

Example 2.

$$\frac{dy}{dx}=-\frac{x+2x^3}{y}.$$

The integral curves $y^2+x^2+x^4=C^2$ are closed ovals ; the origin is their *limiting point* or *centre*.

Example 3.

$$\frac{dy}{dx}=\frac{-x+\mu y-\mu y(x^2+y^2)}{y+\mu x-\mu x(x^2+y^2)}.$$

When transformed into polar co-ordinates, this equation becomes

$$dr=\mu r(r^2-1)d\theta,$$

and the general integral is $r^2(1+Ce^{2\mu\theta})=1$. The integral curves are spirals with the origin as *asymptotic point*.

CHAPTER III

EQUATIONS OF HIGHER DEGREE

18. The General Integral. When the primitive is of the form $f(x, y, C)=0$, involving the arbitrary constant C *implicitly*, the differential equation will arise through elimination of C between the equations

$$f=0, \qquad \frac{\partial f}{\partial x}+\frac{\partial f}{\partial y}y'=0.$$

Only in exceptional cases will the result of this elimination involve y' to the first degree; if the resulting equation

$$F(x, y, y')=0 \quad . \quad . \quad . \quad (18.1)$$

is a polynomial in y', involving y' to the mth power, it is said to be of *degree m*. But it may be irrational in y' or even transcendental.

Theoretically, (18.1) may be solved for y', giving a set of equations

$$y'=F_1(x, y), \quad y'=F_2(x, y), \ldots \quad . \quad (18.2)$$

each of the form hitherto considered. This set may be finite or, in the case of a transcendental equation, infinite in number. If the general integrals of the equations (18.2) are respectively

$$f_1(x, y, C)=0, \quad f_2(x, y, C)=0, \ldots \quad . \quad (18.3)$$

the *general integral* of (18.1) is defined to be any equation $f(x, y, C)=0$ which is satisfied when, and only when, at least one equation (18.3) is satisfied. In particular, when the equation is of degree m, its general integral will be the product of the m integrals (18.3), that is

$$f_1(x, y, C)f_2(x, y, C) \ . \ . \ . \ f_m(x, y, C)=0.$$

In practice, however, the decomposition of (18.1) into (18.2), and the solution of these latter equations, or both, may present difficulties, in which case other lines of approach, some of which will be indicated in the following sections, may be attempted.

Errors in writing and printing are apt to arise through confusion between y' and y; these are obviated by writing p for y', a convention that will be adhered to throughout the present chapter.

Example 1. Let the primitive be the equation of a one-parameter family of straight lines; if the gradient m of each straight line be taken to serve as its parameter, the equation may be written

$$y=mx+f(m),$$

where f is some specified function. Then

$$p=y'=m.$$

Eliminating m, we obtain the differential equation

$$y=px+f(p).$$

In particular, the equation of the family $y=mx+a/m$, where a is a constant, is

$$y=px+a/p$$

or

$$p^2x-py+a=0,$$

of the second degree.

Example 2.

$$p^2-2px+x^2-y^2=0.$$

This equation of the second degree may be decomposed into

$$p-y-x=0, \qquad p+y-x=0.$$

These are linear equations whose general integrals may be written

$$y-Ce^x+x+1=0, \qquad y-Ce^{-x}-x+1=0.$$

Multiplying, we obtain the general integral of the given equation

$$C^2 - C\{e^x(y-x+1)+e^{-x}(y+x+1)\}+(y+1)^2-x^2=0.$$

19. The Clairaut Equation. We consider the equation obtained in the last section (Ex. 1)

$$y=px+f(p), \qquad . \quad . \quad . \quad (19.1)$$

known as the *Clairaut equation*, with a view to discovering whether or not it admits of any integral other than the primitive from which it was derived. Differentiating with respect to x, we obtain

$$p=p+\{x+f'(p)\}\frac{dp}{dx}.$$

This equation may be satisfied in just two ways. On the one hand, we may take $dp/dx=0$, whence $p=C$, and thus recover the primitive

$$y=Cx+f(C). \qquad . \quad . \quad . \quad (19.2)$$

On the other hand, the equation is satisfied if

$$x=-f'(p), \qquad . \quad . \quad . \quad (19.3)$$

and if x is now eliminated from (19.1),

$$y=-pf'(p)+f(p). \qquad . \quad . \quad . \quad (19.4)$$

Equations (19.3) and (19.4) taken together are the parametric equations of an integral curve of (19.1); by eliminating p we obtain the equation of this curve in a form $\phi(x, y)=0$ involving no arbitrary constant. This integral curve represents a *singular solution* (§ 2) of the equation. Since the envelope of the primitive family (19.2) is obtained by eliminating C between that equation and $x+f'(C)=0$, and since the result of this elimination is identical with that of eliminating p between (19.3) and (19.4), it follows that the singular solution may be interpreted geometrically as the envelope of the family of integral curves.

Example 1.

$$y = px + a/p.$$

Differentiating,

$$p = p + (x - a/p^2)dp/dx.$$

Firstly, $dp/dx = 0$ or $p = C$ gives the general integral

$$y = Cx + a/C.$$

Secondly, the alternative $x = a/p^2$ leads to $y = 2a/p$, whence, eliminating p,

$$y^2 = 4ax.$$

Thus the singular solution represents the parabola enveloping the lines $y = Cx + a/C$, and hence the integral curves of the differential equation consist of the parabola together with the aggregate of its tangents. This fact may be confirmed by considering the equation in the form

$$p^2x - py + a = 0;$$

regarded as a quadratic in p, it has real roots only when $y^2 - 4ax \geqslant 0$, *i.e.* outside the parabola there are integral curves (the tangents), inside there are none. The parabola itself is an integral curve separating these two regions.

Example 2. A geometrical problem sometimes leads to a differential equation whose singular integral furnishes the solution aimed at. For instance: *to find a curve such that the tangent at any point makes with the axes a triangle of constant area a^2.* Since the intercepts of the tangent at (x, y) on the x- and y-axes are $x - y/p$, $y - px$ respectively, the differential equation is

$$(x - y/p)(y - px) = 2a^2, \quad \text{or} \quad (y - px)^2 = -2a^2p.$$

This is equivalent to the Clairaut equation

$$y = px \pm a\sqrt{(-2p)},$$

whose singular solution, given parametrically by

$$x = \mp a\sqrt{(-1/2p)}, \qquad y = \pm \tfrac{1}{2}a\sqrt{(-2p)},$$

is $xy = \frac{1}{2}a^2$. Thus the curve sought is a rectangular hyperbola.

20. Generalisation—the d'Alembert Equation. The Clairaut equation is a special case of the more general *d'Alembert equation* (also known as the *Lagrange* equation)

$$y = xg(p) + f(p); \quad . \quad . \quad . \quad (20.1)$$

in fact it is so exceptional a case that it will now be excluded by the stipulation that $g(p)$ is different from p. Differentiating with respect to x, we have

$$p = g(p) + \{xg'(p) + f'(p)\}\frac{dp}{dx}. \quad . \quad . \quad (20.2)$$

Since $g(p)$ does not cancel out with p, we cannot have $dp/dx = 0$ identically, and therefore the general integral curve is not a straight line. Nevertheless, the equation $g(p) - p = 0$ may have real roots; if $p = m$ is one such root dp/dx will be zero, and (20.2) will be satisfied. Thus among the integrals of (20.1) there may be some of the linear form $y = xg(m) + f(m)$, where m is any one of the real roots of $g(p) - p = 0$. It will be shown later (§ 26, Note 2) that these are singular integrals, and not merely special integrals, of the equation.

Since dp/dx is not identically zero, (20.2) may be divided throughout by it, and thus rewritten

$$\{g(p) - p\}\frac{dx}{dp} + g'(p)x + f'(p) = 0.$$

This is a linear equation for x; if

$$\log \phi(p) = \int \frac{dp}{g(p) - p},$$

$\phi(p)$ is an integrating factor, and the general integral is

$$\{g(p) - p\}\phi(p)x = C - \int f'(p)\phi(p)dp. \quad . \quad (20.3)$$

Thus x is expressed in terms of p and the arbitrary constant C; by eliminating x between (20.1) and (20.3), y may be similarly expressed, and thus the general integral may be obtained in terms of p, regarded as a parameter. It is only exceptionally that the parameter can be eliminated and the general integral obtained as a single equation between x, y and C; usually (20.3) taken together with the equation itself must be considered to furnish the general integral.

Example.

$$y = x + p^2 - \tfrac{2}{3}p^3.$$

This is of the above form; differentiating with respect to x,

$$p = 1 + (2p - 2p^2)dp/dx$$

or

$$(p-1)(2p\,dp/dx + 1) = 0.$$

The alternatives are therefore

$$p = 1 \quad \text{and} \quad 2p\,dp + dx = 0.$$

Substituting $p = 1$ in the original equation we find that $y = x + \tfrac{1}{3}$; this solution will be set aside for the moment.

From the second alternative we obtain

$$p^2 + x = C,$$

and, deducing y from the original equation, we may express the general integral as

$$x = C - p^2, \qquad y = C - \tfrac{2}{3}p^3.$$

In this case p can be eliminated, to give the general integral in the form

$$9(C-y)^2 = 4(C-x)^3.$$

The line $y = x + \tfrac{1}{3}$ is not a member of this family of curves, but is their envelope. Consider in particular the intersections of this line with the particular curve ($C = 0$)

$$9y^2 + 4x^3 = 0;$$

the abscissæ are given by

$$(3x+1)^2 + 4x^3 = 0,$$

i.e.

$$4x^3 + 9x^2 + 6x + 1 = 0 \quad \text{or} \quad (x+1)^2(4x+1) = 0.$$

Thus the line touches the particular curve $C = 0$ at a point of abscissa -1; since the other integral curves of the family are derived from this particular one by translation parallel to the line $y = x$ (which leaves the line $y = x + \tfrac{1}{3}$ invariant), every curve of the family touches the line $y = x + \tfrac{1}{3}$, which is their envelope.

21. Further Generalisation. The integration of any differential equation that can be solved algebraically for y in terms of x and p, thus

$$y=f(x, p), \qquad . \quad . \quad . \quad (21.1)$$

may be attempted by the same device of differentiating with respect to x. This gives

$$p=\frac{\partial f}{\partial x}+\frac{\partial f}{\partial p}\frac{dp}{dx}, \qquad . \quad . \quad . \quad (21.2)$$

which is an equation of the first degree in dp/dx; its general integral

$$p=\phi(x, C) \quad \text{or} \quad x=\psi(p, C), \qquad . \quad . \quad (21.3)$$

as the case may be, associated with (21.1) furnishes a parametric general integral of the latter. On the other hand, if $p-\partial f/\partial x$ and $\partial f/\partial p$ have a common factor involving x and p, (21.2) will be satisfied by equating that factor to zero, an equation which may furnish a singular integral of (21.1).

An equation soluble for x, *i.e.* one that can be expressed in the form

$$x=f(y, p),$$

may be attacked in a similar manner by differentiation with respect to y.

Example.

$$y=\frac{x}{x+1}p+\frac{(x+1)e^x}{p}.$$

Differentiating with respect to x:

$$p=\frac{p}{(x+1)^2}+\frac{(x+2)e^x}{p}+\left\{\frac{x}{x+1}-\frac{(x+1)e^x}{p^2}\right\}\frac{dp}{dx},$$

i.e.

$$\left\{\frac{x}{x+1}-\frac{(x+1)e^x}{p^2}\right\}\left\{\frac{dp}{dx}-\frac{x+2}{x+1}p\right\}=0.$$

The second factor gives a differential equation whose general integral is

$$p=C(x+1)e^x;$$

substituting for p in the original we have its general integral

$$y = Cxe^x + 1/C.$$

The first factor gives

$$p^2 = (x+1)^2 e^x/x.$$

On the one hand, integration of this gives $y = 2\sqrt{(xe^x)} + \text{const.}$; on the other, substitution in the original equation gives

$$y^2 = 4xe^x.$$

This is therefore a singular solution; it may be verified to represent the envelope of the integral curves.

22. Equations with One Variable Missing. If an equation of either of the forms

$$F(x, p) = 0 \quad \text{or} \quad G(y, p) = 0$$

is soluble for p, thus

$$p = f(x) \quad \text{or} \quad p = g(y),$$

integration by quadratures is immediate.

On the other hand, we may consider cases in which solution for p is impracticable, but solution for x, or y, is possible. If, for instance, we have

$$x = \phi(p) \quad \text{or} \quad y = \psi(p),$$

the second variable (y or x) is expressible in terms of p by quadratures. Thus if $x = \phi(p)$ we have

$$y - C = \int p\,dx = \int p\phi'(p)\,dp$$

or alternatively

$$y - C = \int p\,dx = px - \int x\,dp = px - \int \phi(p)\,dp,$$

and if $y = \psi(p)$ we have

$$x - C = \int dy/p = \int \psi'(p)\,dp/p$$

or

$$x - C = \int dy/p = y/p + \int y\,dp/p^2 = y/p + \int \psi(p)\,dp/p^2.$$

Another method is to replace the given differential equation by its equivalent in terms of a parameter t. Thus let $G(y, p) = 0$ be equivalent to

$$y = \phi(t), \qquad p = \psi(t).$$

Then
$$x - C = \int \frac{dy}{p} = \int \frac{\phi'(t)dt}{\psi(t)},$$
which, taken with $y = \phi(t)$, gives a parametric representation of the general integral.

Example 1.
$$x^2 = p^2(a^2 - x^2).$$
Solving for x,
$$x = ap/\sqrt{(1+p^2)}; \quad \textit{i.e.} \quad dx = adp/(1+p^2)^{3/2}.$$
Hence
$$y - C = \int pdx = a\int \frac{pdp}{(1+p^2)^{3/2}} = -\frac{a}{\sqrt{(1+p^2)}}.$$
In this case p may be eliminated, giving the general integral
$$x^2 + (y - C)^2 = a^2.$$
Example 2.
$$y = p^2/(p+1).$$
$$x - C = \int dy/p = y/p + \int ydp/p^2$$
$$= y/p + \int dp/(p+1) = y/p + \log | p + 1 |.$$
Example 3.
$$y^2 + p^2 = a^2.$$
This is equivalent to
$$y = a \sin t, \qquad p = a \cos t, \qquad (dy = a \cos t\, dt).$$
Hence
$$dx = dy/p = dt, \quad \textit{i.e.} \quad x - C = t.$$
The general integral is therefore
$$y = a \sin (x - C).$$

23. Homogeneous Equations. Just as a homogeneous equation of the first degree can be reduced to integrable form by the substitution $y = vx$, so also can an equation of the form $F(x, y, p) = 0$, where F is *homogeneous with respect to x and y*. For if the degree of homogeneity is m, $F(x, vx, p) = x^m F(1, v, p) = x^m G(v, p)$ say, and the equation becomes
$$G(v, p) = 0.$$

If it can be solved for p, say $p=\phi(v)$, we have

$$v+x\frac{dv}{dx}=\phi(v),$$

and proceed as in § 4. On the other hand, if it is soluble for v, say $v=\psi(p)$, we write

$$y=vx=x\psi(p),$$

whence, differentiating with respect to x,

$$p=\psi(p)+x\psi'(p)\frac{dp}{dx},$$

i.e.

$$\frac{dx}{x}=\frac{\psi'(p)dp}{p-\psi(p)},$$

and, integrating, we obtain x and thence y in terms of the parameter p.

Example.

$$x^2-k^2y^2+2xyp+(1-k^2)y^2p^2=0.$$

This equation is homogeneous in x and y; writing $y=vx$, cancelling the factor x^2, and solving for p, we have

$$x\frac{dv}{dx}+v=p=\frac{1+k\sqrt{\{1-(k^2-1)v^2\}}}{(k^2-1)v}.$$

The variables v and x are separable; writing $1-(k^2-1)v^2=z^2$ we find

$$\frac{dz}{z+k}+\frac{dx}{x}=0$$

which leads to

$$x(z+k)=C,$$

i.e.

$$x^2z^2=(C-kx)^2$$

or

$$x^2-(k^2-1)y^2=(C-kx)^2.$$

This general integral may be written

$$x^2(1-k^2)+y^2(1-k^2)+2kCx-C^2=0$$

representing a family of circles. As C is quite arbitrary nothing is lost by regarding k as positive throughout.

24. Geometrical Interpretation of a Differential Equation. It will be assumed that $F(x, y, y')$ is a polynomial of degree m in y', and that each coefficient in the polynomial is a one-valued function of x and y.

Let us replace y' by z and interpret x, y, z as co-ordinates in space referred to rectangular axes, with the z-axis vertical. The (x, y)-plane will then be spoken of as the horizontal plane. Consider any point A of co-ordinates (x_0, y_0) in this plane, such that the vertical line through A intersects the surface $F(x, y, z)=0$ in at least one point P; let the height of P above the horizontal plane be z_0. Thus the point A has a definite direction $y'=z_0$ associated with it; if A begins to move forward in this direction, P will begin to move along the surface, but the altering value of z will involve a change in the direction of motion of A.

If, then, we suppose that A moves along the horizontal plane in such a way that the direction of its motion is measured by AP $(y'=z)$, the path traced out by A will be an integral curve of the equation, for it will be a continuous curve such that at every point the relation $F(x, y, y')=0$ is satisfied. This integral curve is the horizontal projection of a certain curve on the surface $F(x, y, z)=0$, such that the condition $y'=z$ or $dy=zdx$ is satisfied throughout its length.

In passing, it may be noted that in the case of the Clairaut equation $y=px+f(p)$, the non-singular integral curves are the projections of the intersections of the surface $y=zx+f(z)$ by the family of parallel planes $z=C$.

To return to the point $A(x_0, y_0)$. A vertical line through A will in general intersect the surface not in one, but in several (though at most m) distinct points. With each of these points is associated a value of z, its height above the horizontal plane, and thus a definite direction y' at A. Consequently, when the points P on the vertical through A are simple intersections with the surface, *i.e.* when the roots of the equation $F(x_0, y_0, z)=0$ are all distinct, integral curves, all with different tangents, will pass through A, equal in number to the real roots of this equation.

Thus through any point (x_0, y_0) of the horizontal plane there will pass at most m integral curves with distinct tangents.

Now consider a point $A(x_0, y_0)$ in the horizontal plane, such that the equation $F(x_0, y_0, z)=0$ has a repeated root. Then we should naturally expect two or more of the integral curves that pass through A to have the same tangent at A. We shall investigate this case more closely, with a view to ascertaining whether or not this supposition agrees with fact.

The analytic condition for the equation

$$F(x_0, y_0, z)=0$$

to have a double or multiple root is that

$$\frac{\partial}{\partial z}F(x_0, y_0, z)=0$$

simultaneously with it. The geometrical condition is that the vertical line through A shall meet the surface in two or more coincident points, *i.e.* shall be a tangent line to the surface.

Let A move so that the vertical line continues to touch the surface; that is to say, in such a way that the equations

$$F(x, y, z)=0, \qquad \frac{\partial}{\partial z}F(x, y, z)=0 \quad . \quad (24.1)$$

are simultaneously satisfied. Then the path of A will be the trace on the horizontal plane of a vertical cylinder enveloping the surface. The most obvious cylinder is that which touches the surface along what is known in descriptive geometry as the visible outline in horizontal projection; its trace forms a natural boundary to the family of integral curves, but, as will be seen, is not necessarily an integral curve itself. There may be other vertical cylinders touching the surface along a curve; their traces will generally cut across the family of integral curves. All possible traces are included in the eliminant of (24.1), which represents a curve or curves, known as the *discriminant locus*.

For *any* displacement (dx, dy, dz) on the surface, we have *

$$F_x dx + F_y dy + F_z dz = 0,$$

but since at any point on the curve of contact of an enveloping cylinder, $F_z = 0$ (24.1), it follows that for any such displacement originating on the curve of contact

$$F_x dx + F_y dy = 0. \qquad (24.2)$$

For a displacement along an integral curve, we have

$$-z dx + dy = 0. \qquad (24.3)$$

If the horizontal projection of the displacement on the surface, at a point (x, y, z) on a curve of contact, is along an integral curve, (24.2) must be consistent with (24.3). Consequently, either $dx = dy = 0$, which implies that the displacement on the surface is vertical, or

$$\begin{vmatrix} F_x & F_y \\ -z & 1 \end{vmatrix} = 0,$$

that is to say,

$$\frac{\partial F}{\partial x} + z\frac{\partial F}{\partial y} = 0 \qquad (24.4)$$

in conjunction with (24.1).

25. Cusp on the Integral Curve. Let us suppose that the equation of the integral curve of $F(x, y, y') = 0$ that passes through (x_0, y_0) can be expressed in terms of a parameter t, thus

$$x = x(t), \qquad y = y(t).$$

* A suffix denotes partial differentiation with respect to the variable in question.

This integral curve will be the projection of a curve

$$x = x(t), \qquad y = y(t), \qquad z = z(t)$$

on the surface, with the condition $dy = z dx$. There will be no loss in generality if we assume that the point (x_0, y_0, z_0) on the curve of contact corresponds to the value $t = 0$.

We shall consider the case of a vertical displacement on the surface from the point (x_0, y_0, z_0), *i.e.* $dx = dy = 0$ when $t = 0$; hence

$$x - x_0 = \tfrac{1}{2}x''(0)t^2 + \tfrac{1}{6}x'''(0)t^3 + \dots$$
$$y - y_0 = \tfrac{1}{2}y''(0)t^2 + \tfrac{1}{6}y'''(0)t^3 + \dots$$
$$z - z_0 = z'(0)t + \dots$$

The approximation to the integral curve in the neighbourhood of (x_0, y_0) is therefore

$$x''(0)(y - y_0) - y''(0)(x - x_0) = \tfrac{1}{6}\{x''(0)y'''(0) - y''(0)x'''(0)\}t^3 + \dots$$
$$= K(x - x_0)^{3/2} + \dots$$

where K is a constant. Thus the integral curve has a *cusp* at the point (x_0, y_0) on the discriminant locus, and the direction of the tangent at the cusp is $y''(0)/x''(0)$. But the direction of the tangent to the discriminant locus itself at (x_0, y_0) is $(-F_x/F_y)_0$. These directions are in general unrelated so that the integral curve does not touch the outline. Thus in this most general case, the discriminant locus is a *cusp-locus*. A more particular case, that of a *tac-locus*, will be discussed briefly in a later section (§ 27).

26. Envelope of Integral Curves. Suppose the condition $dx = dy = 0$ is not satisfied, which (24.4) implies that

$$F_x + zF_y = 0$$

at all points of the curve of contact on the surface. But we also have the condition (24.2)

$$F_x dx + F_y dy = 0,$$

where dy/dx is the direction of a displacement along the

discriminant locus. Therefore this value of dy/dx may be identified with z in $F(x, y, z)=0$; that is to say, the portion of the discriminant locus under consideration is an integral curve of the differential equation $F(x, y, y')=0$. Thus when the curves on the surface which project into the integral curves do not cross the curve of contact vertically, the latter curve projects into a branch of the discriminant locus which is itself an integral curve. If (x, y, z) is a point on the curve of contact, (x, y) will be a point both on the discriminant curve and on one of the general family of integral curves, and these two curves will have a common value of y' at the point, *i.e.* they will have a common tangent. Thus at every point on the discriminant curve in question it will be in contact with one of the general integral curves, and will therefore be an envelope of the family of integral curves. In very special cases the envelope is itself a member of the general family, but in general it is not; it is then known as a *singular integral curve*, representing a singular solution of the equation. To sum up, reverting to the p-notation:

The equation obtained by eliminating p between

$$F(x, y, p)=0 \quad \text{and} \quad F_p(x, y, p)=0 \qquad . \quad (26.1)$$

is known as the *p-discriminant equation*; it represents a curve (the *p-discriminant locus*) of one or more branches in the plane of the general integral curves. A branch will be a *singular integral curve*, *i.e.* an envelope, if and only if the further condition

$$F_x(x, y, p)+pF_y(x, y, p)=0 \quad . \qquad . \quad (26.2)$$

holds at every point. Otherwise the branch is a locus of special points, generally of cusps, on the integral curves.

Note **1.** In the case of the Clairaut equation $px-y+f(p)=0$ or the generalised equation $f(p)+g(px-y)=0$, condition (26.2) is identically satisfied, so that the p-discriminant furnishes the singular solution and nothing else.

Note 2. In the case of $f(p)+xg(p)-y=0$ (20.1) the second of equations (26.1) gives $f'(p)+xg'(p)=0$, which implies (20.2) $g(p)-p=0$. But this is precisely the condition imposed by (26.2), showing that the singular integral curves are straight lines whose gradients are given by the real roots of $g(p)-p=0$.

27. Equation of the Second Degree. Let (x_0, y_0, z_0) be a point on the curve of contact of the surface $F(x, y, z)=0$ with its vertical enveloping cylinder, so that $z=z_0$ is a double root of the equation $F(x_0, y_0, z)=0$, which implies that $F(x_0, y_0, z)$ will have the factor $(z-z_0)^2$. For values of x, y sufficiently near to x_0, y_0, $F(x, y, z)$ will have two factors $z-z_1$, $z-z_2$, where z_1, z_2 are functions of x, y which both become equal to z_0 when $x=x_0$, $y=y_0$. Thus the factor $(z-z_0)^2$ is the limit, as $x \to x_0$, $y \to y_0$ of a quadratic expression $z^2-(z_1+z_2)z+z_1z_2$, and therefore, in the neighbourhood of the p-discriminant, the differential equation $F(x, y, p)=0$ may be regarded as approximated to by a quadratic differential equation $p^2-(z_1+z_2)p+z_1z_2=0$, and thus consideration of such an equation will confirm, and possibly supplement, the discussion of the preceding sections.

We consider, therefore, the following general type of equation of the second degree

$$p^2L(x, y)-2pM(x, y)+N(x, y)=0, \qquad (27.1)$$

and we shall assume that L, M, N are functions developable as ascending power series in x and y. Solving for p, we have

$$p=\frac{M\pm\sqrt{\{M^2-LN\}}}{L}. \qquad (27.2)$$

Thus the (x, y)-plane is divided into distinct regions, namely :

(a) regions for which $M^2 < LN$ in which no integral curves exist ;

(*b*) regions for which $M^2 > LN$, where two distinct real values of p exist for every (x, y), *i.e.* two integral curves with distinct tangents pass through every point.

The two values of p are equal for every point at which

$$M^2 - LN = 0.$$

Now this equation represents a curve which, however, may be composed of several distinct branches. Thus it includes

(*c*) the frontier between the regions (*a*) and (*b*) characterised by the fact that passage across the frontier involves a change in the sign of $M^2 - LN$;

(*d*) curves situated within the regions (*a*) or (*b*) such that $M^2 - LN$ vanishes without a change of sign.

Cusp-Locus. Let the origin O be moved to a point on a branch Γ of the discriminant locus which is a frontier between regions (*a*) and (*b*). Then in the neighbourhood of O,

$$L = l_0 + l_1 x + l_2 y + \dots$$
$$M = m_0 + m_1 x + m_2 y + \dots$$
$$N = n_0 + n_1 x + n_2 y + \dots$$

and $m_0^2 = l_0 n_0$.

Then the gradient of the integral curve that goes through O is (27.2)

$$p = m_0/l_0 = n_0/m_0.$$

But near the origin

$$M^2 - LN = m_0^2 + 2m_0(m_1 x + m_2 y) + \dots$$
$$- l_0 n_0 - l_0(n_1 x + n_2 y) - n_0(l_1 x + l_2 y) - \dots,$$

so that the tangent to Γ at the origin has the equation

$$(2m_0 m_1 - l_0 n_1 - n_0 l_1)x + (2m_0 m_2 - l_0 n_2 - n_0 l_2)y = 0$$

or say $$ax + by = 0.$$

Since $M^2 - LN$ changes sign we may assume that one at least of a and b is not zero. Since $-a/b$ differs in general from m_0/l_0, the slope of Γ at O differs from that of the integral curve, so that Γ is not itself an integral curve. To find how the integral curve through O behaves with respect to Γ, we require a further approximation to (27.2)

$$p=\frac{m_0+m_1x+m_2y+\ .\ .\ .\ \pm\sqrt{(ax+by+\ .\ .\ .)}}{l_0+l_1x+l_2y+\ .\ .\ .}.$$

The first approximation is $p=m_0/l_0$; we therefore write $y=m_0x/l_0+Y$, where Y is of higher degree than the first in x, and obtain an equation of the form

$$\frac{dY}{dx}=\frac{\alpha x+\ .\ .\ .\ \pm\sqrt{(\beta x+\ .\ .\ .)}}{l_0+\ .\ .\ .}=\pm\gamma x^{1/2}+\ .\ .\ .,$$

where α, β, γ are constants. Integrating, we have

$$Y=\pm\tfrac{2}{3}\gamma x^{3/2}+\ .\ .\ .$$

or

$$y=m_0x/l_0\pm\tfrac{2}{3}\gamma x^{3/2}+\ .\ .\ .,$$

so that the integral curve has a cusp on Γ. Hence any branch of the discriminant locus that separates a region of existence from a region of non-existence of integral curves is *in general* a locus of cusps on the integral curves.

Envelope. Now consider the special case when $-a/b=m_0/l_0$. When the substitution

$$y=m_0x/l_0+Y=-ax/b+Y$$

is made, the term in x under the radical disappears, leaving

$$\frac{dY}{dx}=\frac{\alpha x+\ .\ .\ .\ \pm\sqrt{(cx^2+bY+\ .\ .\ .)}}{l_0+\ .\ .\ .}.$$

It will be found impossible to solve this equation by $Y=\lambda x^\mu+\ .\ .\ .$ with $\mu<2$; hence it is of the form

$$Y'=(\beta\pm\gamma)x+\ .\ .\ .,$$

which gives

$$y=m_0x/l_0+\tfrac{1}{2}(\beta\pm\gamma)x^2+\ .\ .\ .,$$

showing that two distinct integral curves touch one another at O. When this happens continuously along a branch of the discriminant curve, since the slope of the latter is everywhere the slope of an integral curve, it is itself an integral curve. So in this case one of the curves having contact is a branch Γ of the discriminant curve, the other is one of the family of integral curves, which are therefore enveloped by Γ.

An application of (26·2) at O gives

$$(p^2l_1 - 2pm_1 + n_1) + p(p^2l_2 - 2pm_2 + n_2) = 0.$$

If each bracket is divided by p and if p is replaced by n_0/m_0 and $1/p$ by l_0/m_0 this reduces to $a + pb = 0$, and therefore if (26.2) holds at any point of Γ, Γ will there touch an integral curve; if it holds at all points of Γ, the Γ will be an envelope of the integral curves.

Tac-Locus. Now suppose that O is moved to a branch Γ of the discriminant curve for which $M^2 - LN$ vanishes without changing sign; the sign on either side of Γ will be assumed to be positive. Then in the neighbourhood of O

$$M^2 - LN = (ax + by)^2 + \ldots$$

The form of the integral curve through O is given approximately by

$$p = \frac{m_0 + m_1x + m_2y + \ldots \pm \sqrt{\{(ax + by)^2 + \ldots\}}}{l_0 + l_1x + l_2y + \ldots}$$

from which we find that

$$y = m_0x/l_0 + (\alpha \pm \beta)x^2 + \ldots$$

Thus two *distinct* integral curves touch one another on the curve Γ. Since the same is true at all its points, Γ is a tac-locus. In general $-a/b$ is not equal to m_0/l_0 and therefore the tac-locus is not an integral curve.

Note 1. The above assumes $M^2 - LN$ to be positive, and the integral curves real on either side of the tac-locus. In the contrary case when $M^2 - LN$ is negative, there will be a real tac-locus of imaginary integral curves.

Note 2. Since the approximation to the tac-locus, at any

point on it, is a squared term, the tac-locus occurs as a squared factor in the p-discriminant.

Example.

$$xp^2 + (y - 3x)p + my = 0.$$

This equation may be solved for y and integrated by the method of § 20. The p-discriminant equation is $(y - 3x)^2 - 4mxy = 0$; the corresponding curve consists of two straight lines through the origin which are real except when $0 < m < -3$, and are coincident when $m = 0$ or -3. The condition for a singular integral (26.2) gives

$$p^2 - 3p + p(p + m) = 0.$$

The first root $p = 0$ would lead to $y = 0$, which is no part of the p-discriminant; the second root $2p = 3 - m$ gives $2y = (3 - m)x$. On substituting this in the p-discriminant equation, we find $m = 1$ (twice) to be the only admissible case, giving $p = 1$, and note that $y = x$ is a solution of the differential equation.

Integrating the differential equation for $m = 1$ in terms of the parameter p, we have

$$x^2 = C(p + 1)^2/p^3, \qquad y^2 = C(p - 3)^2/p$$

or, eliminating p between this expression for y^2 and the differential equation, we obtain the general integral

$$(xy^2 + Cy + 3Cx)(y^3 + 15Cy - 27Cx) + C^2(y - 9x)^2 = 0.$$

We find that $y = x$ has, in fact, contact with all integral curves for which $C > 0$, touching each at two distinct points $x = y = \pm\sqrt{C}$. This contact at two points accounts for the double value of m; it is as if the family of integral curves had two coincident envelopes. Now consider the other branch, $y = 9x$, of the p-discriminant locus; squaring and substituting the above parametric values of x, y we find that the values of p at the points at which $y = 9x$ meets any integral curve are given by

$$(p^2 - 12p - 9)(p^2 + 6p + 9) = 0.$$

The two single values from the first bracket are of no interest, they merely correspond to simple intersections. The double value $p = -3$, however, shows that every integral curve encounters $y = 9x$ in points $x^2 = -4C/27$ at which it has a double tangent. To investigate the behaviour of the integral curve near such a point we put $p = -3 + t$, where t is small, in the parametric expressions for x and y. If $k = \pm\sqrt{(-27/4C)}$ we find

$$x = C^{1/2}(-2+t)(-3+t)^{-3/2}$$

or

$$kx = 1 - \tfrac{1}{24}t^2 - \tfrac{5}{216}t^3 + \ldots$$

$$(3p - p^2)/(p+1) = 9(1 - \tfrac{1}{2}t + \tfrac{1}{18}t^2)(1 - \tfrac{1}{2}t)^{-1}$$

$$= 9(1 + \tfrac{1}{18}t^2 + \tfrac{1}{216}t^3 + \ldots)$$

$$ky = kx(3p - p^2)/(p+1) = 9 + \tfrac{1}{8}t^2 + \tfrac{1}{24}t^3 + \ldots$$

Hence

$$3(kx - 1) + (ky - 9) = -\tfrac{1}{36}t^3 + \ldots$$

and

$$\{3(kx-1) + (ky-9)\}^2 = \tfrac{32}{3}(kx-1)^3 + \ldots$$

Thus every integral curve for which C is negative has a cusp on the line $y = 9x$, the double tangent at the cusp being parallel to $3x + y = 0$. This is an instance where a branch of the p-discriminant locus is a cusp-locus.

To illustrate the circumstances that arise when the p-discriminant locus has a double line, take the case $m = -3$. The general integral is now

$$(xy - C)(y - 3x + C) = 0$$

and thus consists of a family of rectangular hyperbolas and a family of parallel straight lines taken together. The p-discriminant locus is the double line $(y + 3x)^2 = 0$. Now every one of the parallel straight lines touches one hyperbola of the family; in fact $y = 3x - 6\gamma$ touches $xy + 3\gamma^2 = 0$ at the point $x = \gamma$, $y = -3\gamma$ which is a point on the discriminant line. This is a tac-point, or point of contact of two distinct integral curves, and the double line of the p-discriminant is a tac-locus.

CHAPTER IV

EQUATIONS OF THE SECOND AND HIGHER ORDERS

28. Reduction of the Order of an Equation. When we turn to equations of higher order than the first, we discover that there exist certain well-defined types which admit of transformations whereby the order may be lowered. In particular, there are equations that may be reduced, by a transformation of the dependent variable, to allied equations of the first order; if the latter can be integrated, a reversal of the transformation (which usually amounts to one or more quadratures) will lead to the general integral of the former.

There is one small point that may be noted in passing, namely that whereas in an equation of the first order, *e.g.* $Pdx + Qdy = 0$, there is no natural discrimination between the variables, in equations where second and higher derivatives of one variable (y) with respect to the other (x) occur, the distinction is evident. In equations that arise from problems in physics and mechanics, in particular, this distinction arises from a difference in the character of the variable; as when one represents a length and the other represents time.

We shall deal mainly with equations of the second order and shall consider, in particular, those classes in which a change of dependent variable enables a reduction to the first order to be effected. No general discussion of higher orders will be attempted, but when the scope of any process extends beyond the second order, the fact will be mentioned.

The most general differential equation of the second order in which x is independent, and y dependent variable, may be written

$$F(x, y, y', y'')=0. \qquad (28.1)$$

If it may be derived from an equation

$$f(x, y, C, C_1)=0 \qquad (28.2)$$

in which C, C_1 are arbitrary constants, by differentiating twice with respect to x and eliminating these two constants, (28.2) is known as its *primitive*. The elimination of C and C_1 may be performed in either order, but can only lead to the one equation (28.1). For if two such equations were found, y'' could be eliminated between them, leaving an equation of the first order having the primitive (28.2), which cannot be the case unless C and C_1 are specially related. Integration consists of recovering (28.2) or any equivalent expression containing two arbitrary constants, which is a *general integral.*

29. Equations that do not Involve y. The simplest case where reduction of order is possible occurs when the dependent variable y itself is absent from the equation, which may be written

$$F(x, y', y'')=0. \qquad (29.1)$$

We replace y' by p and regard p as a new dependent variable, temporarily replacing y, and thus have

$$F(x, p, p')=0, \qquad (29.2)$$

an equation of the first order in p.

Let us suppose for the moment that this equation can be integrated explicitly, thus

$$p=f(x, C), \qquad (29.3)$$

introducing one arbitrary constant C. We then obtain y by the quadrature

$$y=\int pdx=\int f(x, C)dx+C_1, \qquad (29.4)$$

introducing the second arbitrary constant C_1 and thus arriving at the general integral.

If, on the other hand, the integration of (29.2) gives x more naturally in terms of p, thus

$$x = g(p, C) \qquad . \quad . \quad . \ (29.5)$$

we proceed to take the differential

$$dx = g'(p, C)dp$$

and thus we have

$$y = \int p\,dx = \int p g'(p, C)dp + C_1 \qquad . \quad . \ (29.6)$$

or, alternatively, we may write

$$y = \int p\,dx = px - \int x\,dp = pg(p, C) - \int g(p, C)dp + C_1.$$

Thus x and y are expressed in terms of the parameter p.

When x is absent as well as y, and the equation can be written as

$$y'' = f(y')$$

the process is simplified, for we have

$$p' = f(p) \quad \text{or} \quad dx = dp/f(p).$$

Also $dy = p\,dx = p\,dp/f(p)$ and the general integral is given parametrically by

$$x = \int dp/f(p) + C, \qquad y = \int p\,dp/f(p) + C_1. \quad . \ (29.7)$$

In the case of the equation of order n

$$y^{(n)} = f(y^{(n-1)})$$

we may write $z = y^{(n-1)}$ and thus obtain as in (29.7)

$$x = \int dz/f(z) + C, \qquad y^{(n-2)} = \int z\,dz/f(z) + C_1$$

and then in turn

$$y^{(n-3)} = \int y^{(n-2)}dx = \int y^{(n-2)}dz/f(z)$$

$$= \int \frac{dz}{f(z)} \int z \frac{dz}{f(z)} + C_1 x + C_2$$

$$y^{(n-4)} = \int \frac{dz}{f(z)} \int \frac{dz}{f(z)} \int z \frac{dz}{f(z)} + \tfrac{1}{2}C_1 x^2 + C_2 x + C_3$$

and so on until we arrive at y, which will involve an arbitrary polynomial of degree $n-2$ (involving $n-1$ arbitrary constants).

An equation of the type $F(x, y^{(n-1)}, y^{(n)})=0$ may also be reduced to the first order by writing $z=y^{(n-1)}$.

Example 1.

$$x^2y''=y'^2-2xy'+2x^2.$$

Writing $y'=p$, we have

$$x^2p'=p^2-2xp+2x^2,$$

an equation homogeneous in x and p; if $p=vx$ it reduces to

$$xv'=v^2-3v+2$$

whose integral is

$$Cx=(v-2)/(v-1) \quad \text{whence} \quad v=(Cx-2)/(Cx-1).$$

Thus

$$dy=vxdx=\frac{x(Cx-2)}{Cx-1}=x-\frac{1}{C}\left\{1+\frac{1}{Cx-1}\right\}$$

and finally

$$y=\tfrac{1}{2}x^2-\frac{x}{C}-\frac{1}{C^2}\log|Cx-1|+C_1'.$$

Example 2.

$$2x^2y'y''-xy''+y'=0.$$

Writing $y'=p$ and dividing by x^2 we have

$$2pp'-\frac{p'}{x}+\frac{p}{x^2}=0,$$

which is exact and has the integral

$$p^2-\frac{p}{x}+C=0.$$

We thus obtain

$$x=\frac{p}{p^2+C},$$

whence

$$y=\int pdx=px-\int xdp$$

$$=\frac{p^2}{p^2+C}-\int\frac{pdp}{p^2+C}=\frac{p^2}{p^2+C}-\tfrac{1}{2}\log|p^2+C|+C_1.$$

It is here possible to eliminate p.

Example 3.

$$xy^{\text{iv}} - 2y''' = x^3.$$

The substitution $y''' = z$ gives the linear equation of the first order

$$xz' - 2z = x^3,$$

whence

$$y''' = z = x^3 + Cx^2$$

and in turn

$$y'' = \tfrac{1}{4}x^4 + \tfrac{1}{3}Cx^3 + C_1$$

$$y' = \tfrac{1}{20}x^5 + \tfrac{1}{12}Cx^4 + C_1x + C_2$$

$$y = \tfrac{1}{120}x^6 + \tfrac{1}{60}Cx^5 + \tfrac{1}{2}C_1x^2 + C_2x + C_3.$$

30. Equations that do not Involve x. When the independent variable is lacking, the equation takes the form

$$F(y, y', y'') = 0, \qquad . \qquad . \qquad . \ (30.1)$$

and we again write p for y'. But as y, p are now the variables involved, y'' requires transformation as follows:

$$y'' = \frac{dp}{dx} = \frac{dp}{dy}\frac{dy}{dx} = p\frac{dp}{dy}.$$

Thus the equation becomes

$$F(y, p, pdp/dy) = 0; \qquad . \qquad . \qquad . \ (30.2)$$

it is of the first order with y as independent, and p as dependent variable. If an integral of the form

$$p = f(y, C)$$

is obtainable, we separate the variables, thus:

$$\frac{dy}{f(y, C)} = dx$$

and obtain the general integral

$$x = \int \frac{dy}{f(y, C)} + C_1.$$

On the other hand, when the *first integral* appears in the form

$$y = g(p, C),$$

we have

$$x = \int \frac{dy}{p} = \int \frac{g'(p, C)dp}{p} + C_1$$

or

$$x = \int \frac{dy}{p} = \frac{y}{p} + \int \frac{ydp}{p^2} = \frac{y}{p} + \int \frac{g(p, C)dp}{p^2} + C_1.$$

If y' is absent from an equation of the above type, and it can be expressed in the form

$$y'' = f(y),$$

we write $y'' = pdp/dy$ and multiply by dy, obtaining

$$pdp = f(y)dy.$$

Integrating:

$$p^2 = 2\int f(y)dy + C,$$

whence

$$x = \int \frac{dy}{p} = \int \frac{dy}{\sqrt{\{2\int f(y)dy + C\}}} + C_1.$$

An equation that involves three consecutive derivatives, and nothing else, say $F(y^{(n-2)}, y^{(n-1)}, y^{(n)}) = 0$, may similarly be reduced by taking $y^{(n-2)} = u$, $y^{(n-1)} = z$, $y^{(n)} = zdz/du$.

Example **1.**

$$y(y-1)y'' + y'^2 = 0.$$

The transformed equation is

$$y(y-1)pdp/dy + p^2 = 0.$$

The variables p and y are separable and the first integral is

$$Cp = y/(y-1).$$

Hence

$$x = \int \frac{dy}{p} = C\int \frac{y-1}{y} dy = Cy - C \log | y | + C_1.$$

Example 2.

$$y'' + m^2 y = 0.$$

This becomes

$$p\,dp/dy + m^2 y = 0.$$

Separating the variables and integrating, we have

$$p^2 + m^2 y^2 = m^2 C^2,$$

whence

$$p = \pm m\sqrt{(C^2 - y^2)}$$

or

$$\frac{dy}{\sqrt{(C^2 - y^2)}} = \pm m\,dx$$

and integrating, $\quad \text{arc sin}\,(y/C) = \pm mx + C_1,$

i.e.

$$y = C \sin (C_1 \pm mx)$$

which may also be written as $y = A \cos mx + B \sin mx$.

Example 3.

$$y^{(n-2)} y^{(n)} = \{y^{(n-1)}\}^2.$$

The transformation mentioned above gives

$$uz\,dz/du = z^2 \quad \text{or} \quad dz/z = du/u,$$

whence

$$z = Cu \quad \text{or} \quad u' = Cu.$$

Thus we have

$$y^{(n-2)} = u = C_1 e^{Cx}$$

and integrating $n - 2$ times in succession we obtain the general integral in the form

$$y = Ke^{Cx} + \text{an arbitrary polynomial of degree } n - 3.$$

31. First Homogeneous Type. The expression

$$F(x, y, y', y'')$$

is said to be homogeneous and of degree m *in* y *and its derivatives* if, when λ is any constant,

$$F(x, \lambda y, \lambda y', \lambda y'') = \lambda^m F(x, y, y', y''). \qquad (31.1)$$

When this is the case, the equation $F(x, y, y', y'')=0$ may be reduced, by division throughout by y^m, to one still homogeneous in y, y', y'', but of degree zero. Its form would then be

$$f\left(x, \frac{y'}{y}, \frac{y''}{y}\right)=0. \quad . \quad . \quad . \quad (31.2)$$

The order may now be lowered by taking $y'/y=u$ as a new dependent variable, *i.e.* by the transformation

$$y=e^{\int u dx}$$

which implies $y'=uy$, $y''=y(u'+u^2)$. For the equation then becomes

$$f(x, u, u'+u^2)=0. \quad . \quad . \quad . \quad (31.3)$$

It is now of the first order, but here as in most cases the lowering of order is paid for by an increase in complexity. Thus, when the method is applied to the linear equation

$$y''+p(x)y'+q(x)y=0,$$

which is homogeneous and of the first degree in y, y', y'', it becomes

$$u'+u^2+p(x)u+q(x)=0,$$

a Riccati equation (§ 12) which is actually less manageable than the equivalent linear equation.

When an equation of order n is expressible in the form $f(x, y'/y, \ldots, y^{(n)}/y)=0$, it may be transformed by the above process into an equation of order $n-1$.

Example.

$$xyy''-xy'^2+yy'=0 \quad \text{(second degree in } y, y', y''\text{)}.$$

This may be written

$$x\frac{y''}{y}-x\left(\frac{y'}{y}\right)^2+\frac{y'}{y}=0.$$

The transformed equation is

$$x(u'+u^2)-xu^2+u=0 \quad \text{or} \quad xu'+u=0.$$

Thus we obtain the first integral

$$xu = C \quad \text{or} \quad xy' = Cy$$

and finally arrive at the general integral

$$y = C_1 x^C.$$

32. Second Homogeneous Type. Here $F(x, y, y', y'')$ is homogeneous and of degree m *in* x *and* dx; that is to say, when x is replaced by λx and dx by λdx we have

$$F(\lambda x, y, \lambda^{-1}y', \lambda^{-2}y'') = \lambda^m F(x, y, y', y''). \quad . \quad (32.1)$$

The equation can then always be written in the form

$$f(y, xy', x^2y'') = 0. \quad . \quad . \quad . \quad (32.2)$$

We make the transformation $x = e^t$, so that

$$\frac{dy}{dx} = \frac{dy}{dt}\bigg/\frac{dx}{dt} = \frac{1}{x}\frac{dy}{dt}; \qquad \frac{d^2y}{dx^2} = \frac{1}{x^2}\frac{d^2y}{dt^2} - \frac{1}{x^2}\frac{dy}{dt},$$

and we also write

$$\frac{dy}{dt} = v, \qquad \frac{d^2y}{dt^2} = v\frac{dv}{dy} \quad \text{(as in § 30)}$$

so that (32.2) becomes

$$f(y, v, vdv/dy - v) = 0, \quad . \quad . \quad (32.3)$$

which is of the first order.

An equation of order n which is expressible in the form $f(y, xy', \ldots, x^n y^{(n)}) = 0$ may be reduced in the same way to an equation of order $n - 1$.

Example.

$$xy''(x^2y'' + 2xy' + 2y) + 2yy' = 0.$$

Changing the variables as above, we have

$$\left(v\frac{dv}{dy} - v\right)\left(v\frac{dv}{dy} + v + 2y\right) + 2yv = 0$$

which reduces to

$$v\left(\frac{dv}{dy}\right)^2 + 2y\frac{dv}{dy} - v = 0.$$

If v^2 is taken as dependent variable, this equation becomes of Clairaut type; its integral is

$$v^2 = 4(Cy + C^2),$$

whence, writing $v = xdy/dx$ and separating variables, we have

$$\pm \frac{dy}{2\sqrt{(Cy + C^2)}} = \frac{dx}{x},$$

whence

$$\pm \sqrt{(Cy + C^2)} = C \log C_1 x.$$

Rationalising, the general integral may be written as

$$y = C\{(\log C_1 x)^2 - 1\}.$$

33. Third Homogeneous Type. The characters of the first and second types are here united; $F(x, y, y', y'')$ is homogeneous and of degree m *in* x *and* y *even when these symbols are associated with the differential operator* d. Thus $y' = dy/dx$ is of degree 0 and $y'' = d^2y/dx^2$ is of degree -1, so that

$$F(\lambda x, \lambda y, y', \lambda^{-1} y'') = \lambda^m F(x, y, y', y''). \quad . \quad (33.1)$$

The equation $F(x, y, y', y'') = 0$ may thus be written

$$f(y/x, y', xy'') = 0. \quad . \quad . \quad . \quad (33.2)$$

The transformation $y = xu$ changes it into an equation of the second type, which may be dealt with as in § 32. Another procedure is to make the double change of variable

$$y = xu, \qquad v = xdu/dx,$$

so that

$$y' = u + v,$$

$$xy'' = x\left(1 + \frac{dv}{du}\right)\frac{du}{dx} = v + v\frac{dv}{du}$$

and thus the equation is reduced to

$$f(u, u + v, v + vdv/du) = 0 \quad . \quad . \quad (33.3)$$

of the first order in u and v.

The order of any equation of the type

$$f(y/x, y', \ldots, x^{n-1}y^{(n)}) = 0$$

may be reduced by a unit in this way.

Example.

$$x^2y'' + m(xy' - y)^2 = 0.$$

Writing this equation as $xy'' + m(y' - y/x)^2 = 0$ and making the above transformation, we have

$$v + v\frac{dv}{dx} + mv^2 = 0 \quad \text{or} \quad \frac{dv}{du} + mv + 1 = 0.$$

This linear equation has the integrating factor e^{mu}; we thus obtain

$$e^{mu}(1 + mv) = C,$$

i.e.

$$e^{mu}\left(1 + mx\frac{du}{dx}\right) = C \quad \text{or} \quad \frac{d}{dx}(xe^{mu}) = C.$$

Integrating again, we arrive at the general integral

$$xe^{mu} = Cx + C_1$$

or

$$e^{my/x} = C + C_1/x.$$

34. A Special Case of Homogeneity. An equation *homogeneous in y, xy' and x^2y''* may be written

$$F(xy'/y, x^2y''/y) = 0 \quad \text{or} \quad x^2y'' = yf(xy'/y). \quad . \quad (34.1)$$

It is both of the first and the second type, and therefore also of the third, and may be reduced by taking a new dependent variable u where $u = xy'/y$. Thus we have

$$xy' = uy, \qquad xy'' = u'y + (u - 1)y',$$

i.e.

$$x^2y'' = u'xy + u(u - 1)y,$$

and so the equation, in its second form, becomes

$$xu' + u(u - 1) = f(u).$$

The variables are separable, giving

$$\frac{dx}{x}=\frac{du}{f(u)-u(u-1)} \quad \text{and hence} \quad \frac{dy}{y}=\frac{udu}{f(u)-u(u-1)}. \tag{34.2}$$

Integrating, we obtain a parametric representation of x and y in terms of u, involving two constants of integration. Alternatively we may integrate the first equation and obtain $x=\phi(u, C)=\phi(xy'/y, C)$. Solving for xy'/y we obtain an equation whose variables are separable.

Example 1. The *Euler linear equation* of the second order

$$x^2y''-(\alpha+\beta-1)xy'+\alpha\beta y=0,$$

where α, β are constants, is of this type. The above transformation leads to

$$xu'+(u-\alpha)(u-\beta)=0,$$

whence, separating variables and integrating,

$$\frac{u-\alpha}{u-\beta}=Cx^{\alpha-\beta}$$

or

$$\frac{C\alpha x^{\alpha}-\beta x^{\beta}}{Cx^{\alpha}-x^{\beta}}=u=\frac{xy'}{y},$$

i.e.

$$\frac{d(Cx^{\alpha}-x^{\beta})}{Cx^{\alpha}-x^{\beta}}=\frac{dy}{y},$$

whence $y=C_1(Cx^{\alpha}-x^{\beta})$, that is to say the general integral may be written $y=Ax^{\alpha}+Bx^{\beta}$, where A and B are arbitrary constants.

Example 2.

$$xyy''=y'(2xy'+ay).$$

Taking this equation in the form

$$x^2y''=y\frac{xy'}{y}\left(2\frac{xy'}{y}+a\right)$$

and applying the same transformation, we obtain

$$xu'=u(u+a+1)$$

whence

$$\frac{dx}{x}=\frac{du}{u(u+a+1)}; \qquad \frac{dy}{y}=\frac{du}{u+a+1};$$

$$x^{a+1}=C\frac{u}{u+a+1}; \qquad y=C_1(u+a+1).$$

By eliminating u, the general integral may be expressed in the form

$$y=1/(A+Bx^{a+1}).$$

35. First Integral. The term first integral has been used to denote (§ 30) the differential equation of the first order, involving one arbitrary constant, that results from transforming a differential equation of the second order into one of the first, and integrating the latter. When the first integral is obtainable by immediate integration of the differential equation, the latter is said to be *exact*. Thus

$$2y'y''+xy'+y=0$$

is exact and its first integral is

$$y'^2+xy=C.$$

In the same way, a first integral of an equation of order n

$$F(x, y, y', y'', \ldots, y^{(n)})=0 \qquad (35.1)$$

will be an equation of order $n-1$

$$F_1(x, y, y', y'', \ldots, y^{(n-1)}, C)=0, \qquad (35.2)$$

where C is arbitrary. Moreover, when $dF_1/dx=F$, then $F=0$ is exact.

As in the case of equations of the first order, when an equation of any order is not exact as it stands, it may be rendered exact by the introduction of an *integrating factor*. For example, the equation

$$y''+P(x, y)y'+Q(x, y)y'^2=0$$

admits of the integrating factor $1/y'$ whenever $Pdx+Qdy$ is an exact differential, and the first integral then is *

$$\log|y'|+\int(Pdx+Qdy)=C.$$

A differential equation of the second order has two distinct first integrals. For let the primitive be $f(x, y, A, B)=0$, where A, B are *distinct* arbitrary constants (distinct in the sense of not being replaceable by a single constant C, as would be the case, for example, if A, B occurred only in the combination $A+B$). By differentiating the primitive we obtain an equation $\phi(x, y, y', A, B)=0$, and then by eliminating B and A in turn between $f=0$, $\phi=0$ we arrive at

$$F_1(x, y, y', A)=0, \qquad F_2(x, y, y', B)=0$$

which are formally distinct because A and B are distinct in the primitive. By differentiating again and eliminating A, B between the two resulting equations and the primitive we reach the differential equation

$$F(x, y, y', y'')=0.$$

Integrating the differential equation once results in the recovery of either $F_1=0$ or $F_2=0$ or an equivalent. Thus $F_1=0$, $F_2=0$ are first integrals, and we see that two distinct ones exist. If, by adopting two separate methods of integration we recover both $F_1=0$ and $F_2=0$, we obtain the primitive by eliminating y' between them. There cannot be more than two distinct first integrals, for if $F_3=0$ were a third, a distinct primitive would be obtained by eliminating y' between $F_1=0$, $F_3=0$. But the existence theorems prove, what we shall here regard as a postulate, that there cannot be more than one distinct primitive

* The equation is also integrable (i) when P and Q are functions of x alone, for it is then equivalent to a Bernoulli equation in p, (ii) when P and Q are functions of y alone, for then it may be reduced to a linear equation in the variables y and p.

dependent upon a set of arbitrary constants equal in number to the order of the equation, *i.e.* there cannot be more than one distinct general integral.

Therefore an equation of the second order has just two distinct first integrals.

Example. The equation

$$y'' + m^2 y = 0 \qquad (\S\ 30, \text{Ex. } 2)$$

has, among others, the following integrating factors:

$$\cos mx, \qquad \sin mx, \qquad 2y'$$

which lead to the corresponding first integrals:

$$y' \cos mx + my \sin mx = A,$$
$$y' \sin mx - my \cos mx = B,$$
$$y'^2 + m^2 y^2 = C^2.$$

By eliminating y' between the first two we obtain the general integral

$$my = A \sin mx + B \cos mx.$$

The third may be obtained from the first two by squaring and adding; the relation between the constants is $A^2 + B^2 = C^2$.

36. Problems Involving Curvature. The geometrical problems previously discussed (§§ 14, 15) depended upon a relationship between the slope y' and the co-ordinates (x, y) which was imposed at every point of a plane curve. Such problems thus led to differential equations of the first order. We now consider problems in which the curvature at every point obeys a specified law.

The radius of curvature at the point (x, y) is

$$\rho = \frac{(1 + y'^2)^{3/2}}{y''};$$

the centre of curvature (ξ, η) relative to that point is given by

$$\xi = x - \frac{y'(1 + y'^2)}{y''}, \qquad \eta = y + \frac{1 + y'^2}{y''}.$$

The locus of the centre of curvature is the *evolute*. A whole family of parallel curves have the same evolute; they are its *involutes*.

As the above expressions involve y'', a problem that depends essentially upon curvature will involve the integration of a differential equation of the second order.

As an example, we consider *Curves whose Radius of Curvature is proportional to the Normal.*

The length of the normal is understood to be the length of that portion intercepted between the curve and the x-axis, which is given by $y(1+y'^2)^{1/2}$. Thus if the normal is n times the radius of curvature, we have

$$y(1+y'^2)^{1/2} = \pm n\frac{(1+y'^2)^{3/2}}{y''}$$

or

$$yy'' = \pm n(1+y'^2).$$

The ambiguous sign arises from the fact that each of the two lengths in question may be measured in either of two directions. Let us agree to measure them both away from the curve. If the curve were, at the point considered, above the x-axis, and concave upwards, both y and y'' would be positive, but the normal and radius of curvature would run in opposite directions. Hence our convention demands the negative sign.

The equation to which the problem has been reduced is therefore

$$yy'' = -n(1+y'^2).$$

Since x is absent, we write (§ 30)

$$y' = p, \qquad y'' = p\,dp/dy$$

and obtain

$$yp\,dp = -n(1+p^2)dy.$$

Separating the variables and integrating, we obtain

$$1+p^2 = \left(\frac{a}{y}\right)^{2n},$$

whence

$$x=\int\frac{dy}{p}=\int\frac{dy}{\sqrt{\left\{\left(\frac{a}{y}\right)^{2n}-1\right\}}}+b,$$

where a and b are the constants of integration.

We take two cases where the radius of curvature has the same direction as the normal ($n=1, \frac{1}{2}$) and two cases in which the directions are opposed ($n=-1, -\frac{1}{2}$).

When $n=1$,

$$x=\int\frac{ydy}{\sqrt{(a^2-y^2)}}+b=-\sqrt{(a^2-y^2)}+b$$

or

$$(x-b)^2+y^2=a^2.$$

Thus any *circle* with its centre on the x-axis satisfies the condition; in fact the normal and the radius are coincident.

When $n=\frac{1}{2}$,

$$x=\int\sqrt{\left\{\frac{y}{a-y}\right\}}dy+b.$$

Write $y=a\sin^2\theta$, $dy=2a\sin\theta\cos\theta$; then

$$x-b=2a\int\sin^2\theta\,d\theta=a\int(1-\cos 2\theta)d\theta=a(\theta-\tfrac{1}{2}\sin 2\theta)$$

or, if $2\theta=\phi$,

$$x=b+\tfrac{1}{2}a(\phi-\sin\phi),\qquad y=\tfrac{1}{2}a(1-\cos\phi).$$

Thus the curve whose radius of curvature is twice its normal, and in the same direction as the normal, is a *cycloid*.

When $n=-1$,

$$x=\int\frac{ady}{\sqrt{(y^2-a^2)}}+b=a\operatorname{arg\,cosh}\frac{y}{a}+b$$

or

$$y=a\cosh\frac{x-b}{a}.$$

Thus when the radius of curvature equals the normal, but is oppositely directed, the curve is a *catenary*.

When $n = -\frac{1}{2}$,

$$x = \int \sqrt{\left\{\frac{a}{y-a}\right\}} dy + b = 2\sqrt{a(y-a)} + b$$

or

$$(x-b)^2 = 4a(y-a).$$

So when the radius of curvature is twice the normal, but is oppositely directed, the curve is a *parabola* with its axis perpendicular to the x-axis, and its latus rectum equal to four times the ordinate of its vertex.

CHAPTER V

LINEAR EQUATIONS

37. Form of the General Integral. An equation of order n is said to be *linear* if it is linear in the dependent variable y and the derivatives $y', y'', \ldots, y^{(n)}$. Thus the most general linear equation of order n is of the form

$$p_0(x)\frac{d^ny}{dx^n}+p_1(x)\frac{d^{n-1}y}{dx^{n-1}}+\ldots+p_{n-1}(x)\frac{dy}{dx}+p_n(x)y=f(x). \qquad (37.1)$$

If D denotes the differential operator $d()/dx$, the left-hand member is derived from y by the compound operator

$$p_0(x)D^n+p_1(x)D^{n-1}+\ldots+p_{n-1}(x)D+p_n(x),$$

and if L is written for this operator, the equation assumes the convenient abbreviated form

$$Ly=f(x). \qquad . \quad . \quad . \ (37.2)$$

We take it for granted that since the equation is of order n, its general integral will depend on n distinct arbitrary constants, and proceed to consider the mode of this dependence.

Let us suppose that two distinct particular integrals of (37.2) are known, say $y=y_1$ and $y=y_2$. Then

$$Ly_1=f(x), \qquad Ly_2=f(x),$$

i.e.

$$Ly_2-Ly_1=0.$$

Now since $p(x)D^r(y_2-y_1)=p(x)D^ry_2-p(x)D^ry_1$, and since

$Ly_2 - Ly_1$ is merely a sum of terms like this, we have

$$L(y_2 - y_1) = Ly_2 - Ly_1 = 0.$$

Thus if u represents the difference between any two solutions of (37.2), u will satisfy the *reduced* equation

$$Lu = 0, \quad . \quad . \quad . \quad . \quad (37.3)$$

which contains no term free from u or a derivative of u. Thus we are led to consider, first of all, the general solution of this reduced equation.

In the first place we observe that if C is any constant, $p(x)D^r(Cu) = Cp(x)D^r u$, and remembering the composition of the operator L we conclude that $L(Cu) = CLu$. So if $u = u_1$ is any solution of $Lu = 0$, we have $L(C_1u_1) = C_1Lu_1 = 0$, and therefore C_1u_1 is an integral, whatever the constant C_1 may be.

Next we note that if we have a number of particular integrals $u_1, u_2, u_3, \ldots$ then whatever the constants $C_1, C_2, C_3, \ldots$ may be,

$$L(C_1u_1 + C_2u_2 + C_3u_3 + \ldots) = C_1Lu_1 + C_2Lu_2 + C_3Lu_3 + \ldots = 0$$

that is, $C_1u_1 + C_2u_2 + C_3u_3 + \ldots$ is also an integral.

Functions $u_1, u_2, u_3, \ldots$ are said to be *linearly independent* if it is impossible to find constants $C_1, C_2, C_3, \ldots$ *not all zero* such that

$$C_1u_1 + C_2u_2 + C_3u_3 + \ldots = 0$$

identically. For example, the three functions $\sin^2 x$, $\cos^2 x$, $\sin 2x$ are linearly independent, for no relation of the type $A \sin^2 x + B \cos^2 x + C \sin 2x = 0$ links them.* But $\sin^2 x$, $\cos^2 x$, $\cos 2x$ are not linearly independent, for $\sin^2 x - \cos^2 x + \cos 2x = 0$ identically.

Now if $u_1, u_2, \ldots, u_n$ form a set of linearly independent integrals of (37.3), then $u = C_1u_1 + C_2u_2 + \ldots + C_nu_n$ will be a solution, and since it is not identically zero for any

* Assuming the relation, we put $x = 0$ and find $B = 0$; then $x = \pi/2$ and find $A = 0$; it then follows that $C = 0$.

choice of $C_1, C_2, \ldots, C_n$ (not all zero), and also since it contains the full complement of n arbitrary constants, it will be the general integral of the *reduced* equation (37.3). Any such set of n linearly distinct integrals is said to be a *fundamental set.*

Returning now to the original unreduced equation (37.2) let $y=\eta$ be *any* particular integral, involving no arbitrary constant, and let $y=Y$ be the general integral. Then $u=Y-\eta$ will satisfy the reduced equation, and will contain n arbitrary constants; it will in fact be the general integral of the reduced equation, and we have

$$Y=C_1u_1+C_2u_2+\ \ldots\ +C_nu_n+\eta.$$

Thus the general integral of the unreduced equation has two components, namely (i) the general solution of the reduced equation, involving n arbitrary constants, and known as the *complementary function,* (ii) a *particular integral* involving no arbitrary constant.

Example.

$x(x^2+1)^2y''-(3x^2-1)(x^2+1)y'+4x(x^2-1)y=x^4-6x^2+1.$

The reduced equation

$$x(x^2+1)^2u''-(3x^2-1)(x^2+1)u'+4x(x^2-1)u=0$$

has two independent particular solutions

$$x^2+1, \qquad (x^2+1)\log x.$$

Thus its general solution is

$$u=(x^2+1)(A+B\log x).$$

A particular integral of the original is x; the general solution therefore is

$$y=(x^2+1)(A+B\log x)+x,$$

where A and B are arbitrary constants.

38. Depression of the Order. When any integral of a reduced equation of order n is known, the equation can be transformed into another (also linear and reduced) of order $n-1$. If the known integral is u_1, the transformation is $u=u_1\int v dx$, where v is a new dependent variable. This transformation, and the proof, are general, but for brevity we take an equation of the third order

$$p_0u''' + p_1u'' + p_2u' + p_3u = 0, \quad . \quad . \quad (38.1)$$

where p_0, p_1, p_2, p_3 are functions of x, or constants. Substituting

$$u = u_1\int v dx, \qquad u' = u_1'\int v dx + u_1v, \qquad u'' = u_1''\int v dx + 2u_1'v + u_1v',$$
$$u''' = u_1'''\int v dx + 3u_1''v + 3u_1'v' + u_1v'',$$

and rearranging we have

$$(p_0u_1''' + p_1u_1'' + p_2u_1' + p_3u_1)\int v dx$$
$$+ (3p_0u_1'' + 2p_1u_1' + p_2u_1)v + (3p_0u_1' + p_1u_1)v' + p_0u_1v'' = 0.$$

Since u_1 is an integral of (38.1) the first term disappears, leaving a reduced linear equation of the second order in v.

Example.

$$xy'' - (2x+1)y' + (x+1)y = 0.$$

A particular integral is e^x; writing $y = e^x\int v dx$,

$$y' = e^x\left(\int v dx + v\right), \qquad y'' = e^x\left(\int v dx + 2v + v'\right),$$

we obtain an equation which reduces to

$$xv' - v = 0$$

giving

$$v = 2Ax, \qquad \int v dx = Ax^2 + B,$$
$$y = e^x(Ax^2 + B).$$

39. Reduced Equation with Constant Coefficients. As no loss in generality results from taking the leading coefficient to be unity, the equation may be written as

$$(D^n + a_1D^{n-1} + \ . \ . \ . \ + a_{n-1}D + a_n)u = 0, \qquad (39.1)$$

where $a_1, \ . \ . \ ., a_n$ are constants, or in short as

$$F(D)u = 0. \quad . \quad . \quad . \quad (39.2)$$

Now $F(D)$ is a polynomial, not in an algebraic symbol, but in the differential operator D; the laws of algebra must therefore not be applied without justification. Our first step will be to show that $F(D)$ can be factorised in the same way, and with the same result, as if D were an ordinary symbol of algebra. Consider the product

$$(D-\alpha)(D-\beta)$$

in which α, β are constant numbers, real or complex, and let X be any function of x that can be differentiated at least twice. Then

$$\begin{aligned}(D-\alpha)(D-\beta)X &= \left(\frac{d}{dx}-\alpha\right)\left(\frac{dX}{dx}-\beta X\right)\\ &= \frac{d^2X}{dx^2}-(\alpha+\beta)\frac{dX}{dx}+\alpha\beta X\\ &= \{D^2-(\alpha+\beta)D+\alpha\beta\}X.\end{aligned}$$

But we likewise have

$$(D-\beta)(D-\alpha)X=\{D^2-(\alpha+\beta)D+\alpha\beta\}X.$$

As these relations are independent of X, we conclude that *

$$D^2-(\alpha+\beta)D+\alpha\beta=(D-\alpha)(D-\beta)=(D-\beta)(D-\alpha),$$

where the sign of equality denotes equality of *effect*, not of magnitude. Thus any operator of the second order with constant coefficients may be factorised in the ordinary algebraical sense, into two linear factors, and these factors are *permutable*; that is, their order is immaterial. By repeating the argument with three factors $D-\alpha$, $D-\beta$, $D-\gamma$, we show that an operator of the third order can be decomposed into the product of three linear operators taken in any order, and, in fact, should find no difficulty, other than the labour of writing, in proving that the general operator of order n is the equivalent of a product of n linear operators.

* Note that if α, β were not constants, these relations might not be true. Thus $(D-x)(D-1)=D^2-(x+1)D+x$, but $(D-1)(D-x)=D^2-(x+1)D+x-1$.

We shall assume that the coefficients $a_1, \ldots, a_n$ in (39.1) are real, so that the numbers α, β, γ, in the linear factors of $F(D)$ are either real or paired as conjugate complex numbers. Let $D-\alpha$ be any linear factor of $F(D)$, so that the equation may be written as

$$F_1(D)(D-\alpha)u=0,$$

where $F_1(D)$ is the co-factor of $D-\alpha$ in $F(D)$. Now this equation is certainly satisfied if $(D-\alpha)u=0$, *i.e.* when

$$u=Ae^{\alpha x},$$

where A is an arbitrary constant (not necessarily real). By rearranging the factors so that $D-\beta$ comes last we obtain another solution $u=Be^{\beta x}$. Continuing in this way, we conclude that (39.2) is satisfied by

$$u=Ae^{\alpha x}, \qquad u=Be^{\beta x}, \qquad u=Ce^{\gamma x}$$

individually, and is therefore also satisfied by

$$u=Ae^{\alpha x}+Be^{\beta x}+Ce^{\gamma x}+\ldots$$

If $F(D)$ has n *distinct* linear factors $D-\alpha, \ldots, D-\kappa$, we should in this manner obtain the solution

$$u=Ae^{\alpha x}+\ldots+Ke^{\kappa x}$$

containing n arbitrary constants $A, \ldots, K$, and this expression will furnish the general integral of (39.2) provided that its n terms are linearly independent.

Assume for the moment that they are not linearly independent; that is, assume that $A, B, \ldots, K$ can be determined so that

$$Ae^{\alpha x}+Be^{\beta x}+\ldots+Ke^{\kappa x}=0$$

identically. Differentiating $n-1$ times in succession we obtain the $n-1$ further identities

$$A\alpha e^{\alpha x}+B\beta e^{\beta x}+\ldots+K\kappa e^{\kappa x}=0,$$

$$\cdots\cdots\cdots$$

$$A\alpha^{n-1}e^{\alpha x}+B\beta^{n-1}e^{\beta x}+\ldots+K\kappa^{n-1}e^{\kappa x}=0.$$

Eliminating $Ae^{\alpha x}$, $Be^{\beta x}$, . . ., $Ke^{\kappa x}$ between the set of n identities, we have the condition

$$\begin{vmatrix} 1, & 1, & \ldots, & 1 \\ \alpha, & \beta, & \ldots, & \kappa \\ \ldots & & \ldots, & \ldots \\ \alpha^{n-1}, & \beta^{n-1}, & \ldots, & \kappa^{n-1} \end{vmatrix} = 0$$

or (*v.* Aitken, *Determinants and Matrices*, p. 41)

$$\Pi(\alpha - \beta) = 0,$$

where $\Pi(\alpha - \beta)$ symbolises the product of all the differences $\alpha - \beta$, $\alpha - \gamma$, $\beta - \gamma$, etc. As it is zero, one at least of these differences must be zero, contrary to the hypothesis that α, β, . . ., κ are all unequal. Thus $e^{\alpha x}$, $e^{\beta x}$, . . ., $e^{\kappa x}$ are linearly independent, and form a fundamental set, provided that no two of α, β, . . ., κ are equal. The case of repeated factors in $F(D)$ will be deferred to later sections (§§ 42, 43).

The form of general solution that has been obtained suggests that the most direct method of dealing with an equation of the form $F(D)u = 0$ is to adopt as a tentative solution

$$u = e^{rx},$$

where r is a constant to be determined. Since

$$Du = re^{rx} = ru, \qquad D^2u = r^2u, \ldots, \qquad D^nu = r^nu,$$

we should have

$$F(D)u = F(r)u.$$

Thus $u = e^{rx}$ will be a particular solution if $F(r) = 0$. Solving this algebraic equation (the *auxiliary* equation) we obtain as many of the exponential terms belonging to the general integral as it has distinct roots, but when repeated roots are present, the solution is incomplete.

Example.

$$y''' - 2y'' - 5y' + 6y = 0.$$

G

The auxiliary equation

$$r^3 - 2r^2 - 5r + 6 = 0$$

has three distinct roots, $r = -2, 1, 3$. Hence the general integral is

$$y = Ae^{-2x} + Be^{x} + Ce^{3x}.$$

40. Properties of the Operator $F(D)$. In what follows it will be necessary to apply a polynomial operator to a function of the form $e^{ax}X$, where X is a function of x, at present unspecified except for the stipulation that it shall be differentiable at least n times.

We have

$$D \,.\, e^{ax}X = ae^{ax}X + e^{ax}DX = e^{ax}(D+a)X,$$
$$D^2 \,.\, e^{ax}X = D\{e^{ax}(D+a)X\} = e^{ax}(D+a)^2X,$$

and in general

$$D^r \,.\, e^{ax}X = e^{ax}(D+a)^rX \qquad (r = 1, 2, \ldots, n).$$

Similarly, it may be proved that

$$(D-a)^r \,.\, e^{ax}X = e^{ax}D^rX.$$

More generally, if $F(D)$ is any polynomial of degree n in D,

$$\begin{aligned} F(D) \,.\, e^{ax}X &= \{D^n + a_1D^{n-1} + \ldots + a_{n-1}D + a_n\}e^{ax}X \\ &= D^n \,.\, e^{ax}X + a_1D^{n-1} \,.\, e^{ax}X + \ldots \\ &\qquad + a_{n-1}D \,.\, e^{ax}X + a_ne^{ax}X \\ &= e^{ax}(D+a)^nX + a_1e^{ax}(D+a)^{n-1}X + \ldots \\ &\qquad + a_{n-1}e^{ax}(D+a)X + a_ne^{ax}X \\ &= e^{ax}F(D+a)X. \qquad (40.1) \end{aligned}$$

At times it is necessary to operate on $\cos \beta x$ or $\sin \beta x$. We then have

$$D \cos \beta x = -\beta \sin \beta x, \qquad D \sin \beta x = \beta \cos \beta x,$$
$$D^2 \cos \beta x = -\beta^2 \cos \beta x, \qquad D^2 \sin \beta x = -\beta^2 \sin \beta x,$$

and in general

$$D^{2m} \cos \beta x = (-\beta^2)^m \cos \beta x, \qquad D^{2m} \sin \beta x = (-\beta^2)^m \sin \beta x.$$

Thus if $G(D^2)$ is any polynomial in D^2 (not merely in D) we have

$$G(D^2)\cos\beta x = G(-\beta^2)\cos\beta x,$$
$$G(D^2)\sin\beta x = G(-\beta^2)\sin\beta x.$$

Now any polynomial containing both even and odd powers of D may be written

$$F(D) = G(D^2) + DH(D^2) = G(D^2) + H(D^2)D,$$

and so

$$\begin{aligned} F(D)\cos\beta x &= G(D^2)\cos\beta x + H(D^2)D\cos\beta x \\ &= G(-\beta^2)\cos\beta x + H(D^2)(-\beta\sin\beta x) \\ &= G(-\beta^2)\cos\beta x - \beta H(-\beta^2)\sin\beta x \end{aligned}$$

with analogous results for $F(D)\sin\beta x$ and, more generally, for $F(D)\sin(\beta x + \epsilon)$, where ϵ is constant.

41. Pairs of Conjugate Factors. Suppose that among the factors of $F(D)$ there occurs the conjugate imaginary pair $D - a + \beta i$, $D - a - \beta i$, which together constitute the real quadratic factor $(D-a)^2 + \beta^2$. Then the equation $F(D)u = 0$ may be expressed as

$$F_2(D)\{(D-a)^2 + \beta^2\}u = 0,$$

where $F_2(D)$ is a polynomial of degree $n-2$ in D; it is satisfied if u is such that

$$\{(D-a)^2 + \beta^2\}u = 0.$$

Let $u = e^{ax}v$, so that $(D-a)^2 e^{ax}v = e^{ax}D^2 v$, and v must satisfy

$$(D^2 + \beta^2)v = 0.$$

The previous section shows (see also §§ 30, 35) that the general solution of this equation is $v = A\cos\beta x + B\sin\beta x$. Thus the contribution of the quadratic factor $(D-a)^2 + \beta^2$ to the complementary function is

$$e^{ax}(A\cos\beta x + B\sin\beta x).$$

The same result may be obtained by the use of imaginary

exponents. The factor $D-\alpha+\beta i$ contributes the partial solution

$$u_1=e^{(\alpha-\beta i)x}=e^{\alpha x}e^{-i\beta x}=e^{\alpha x}(\cos\beta x-i\sin\beta x);$$

the factor $D-\alpha-\beta i$ contributes similarly

$$u_2=e^{\alpha x}(\cos\beta x+i\sin\beta x).$$

Thus $\frac{1}{2}(u_1+u_2)=e^{\alpha x}\cos\beta x$ and $\frac{1}{2}i(u_1-u_2)=e^{\alpha x}\sin\beta x$ are constituents of the complementary function.

Example 1.

$$y'''+6y'+20y=0.$$

This equation may be written as

$$(D^3+6D+20)y=0,$$

i.e.

$$(D+2)(D^2-2D+10)y=(D+2)\{(D-1)^2+9\}y=0.$$

Hence the general integral:

$$y=Ae^{-2x}+e^{x}\{B\cos 3x+C\sin 3x\}.$$

Example 2.

$$y^{\text{iv}}-y=0$$

$$(D^4-1)y=(D^2+1)(D-1)(D+1)y=0$$

$$y=A\cos x+B\sin x+Ce^{x}+C'e^{-x}.$$

Example 3.

$$y^{\text{iv}}+4m^4y=0$$

$$(D^4+4m^4)y=(D^2-2mD+2m^2)(D^2+2mD+2m^2)y=0$$

$$y=e^{mx}(A\cos mx+B\sin mx)+e^{-mx}(A_1\cos mx+B_1\sin mx).$$

This may also be written

$$y=C_1\cosh mx\cos mx+C_2\cosh mx\sin mx+C_3\sinh mx\cos mx+C_4\sinh mx\sin mx.$$

42. Repeated Real Factors. A repeated real factor in the polynomial $F(D)$ implies that two or more of the numbers α, β, . . . are equal and that the number of linearly distinct exponentials $e^{\alpha x}$, $e^{\beta x}$, . . . falls below n. We shall now indicate how this deficiency is to be supplied.

Let the factor $D-a$ occur r-fold, so that the equation $F(D)u=0$ may be written

$$F_r(D)(D-a)^r u=0, \quad . \quad . \quad . \quad (42.1)$$

where $F_r(D)$ is a polynomial in D of degree $n-r$. Thus a complete solution of the equation

$$(D-a)^r u=0, \quad . \quad . \quad . \quad (42.2)$$

which is what we now seek, will satisfy the original. A partial solution is $u=Ae^{ax}$; tentatively we replace the constant A by a variable v dependent upon x, thus

$$u=ve^{ax}.$$

But

$$(D-a)^r u=e^{ax}D^r v$$

and so (42.2) will be satisfied if v is such that $D^r v=0$; that is, v may be any arbitrary polynomial of degree $r-1$ in x, say

$$v=A+Bx+Cx^2+\ . \ . \ . \ +Hx^{r-1},$$

and therefore the contribution of the factor $(D-a)^r$ to the complementary function is

$$u=(A+Bx+Cx^2+\ . \ . \ . \ +Hx^{r-1})e^{ax}.$$

Its terms are linearly independent, and it contains r arbitrary constants, and so it is the full contribution of that factor. The $n-r$ remaining terms of the complementary function are given by

$$F_r(D)u=0.$$

Example 1.

$$y'''-3y'+2y=0$$

$$(D+2)(D-1)^2 y=0$$

$$y=e^x(A+Bx)+Ce^{-2x}.$$

Example 2.

$$y^{\text{iv}}-2y''+y=0$$

$$(D-1)^2(D+1)^2 y=0$$

$$y=e^x(A+Bx)+e^{-x}(A_1+B_1x).$$

43. Repeated Complex Factors. Let the quadratic factor $(D-a)^2+\beta^2$ occur r-fold; then $F(D)$ will have the two repeated complex factors $(D-a+\beta i)^r$, $(D-a-\beta i)^r$. The contribution of the former will be

$$u_1 = e^{ax}(\cos \beta x + i \sin \beta x)M(x),$$

and of the latter

$$u_2 = e^{ax}(\cos \beta x - i \sin \beta x)M_1(x),$$

where $M(x)$, $M_1(x)$ are independent arbitrary polynomials of degree $r-1$. Thus their united contribution, which is that of the repeated quadratic factor, will be of the form

$$u = (A + Bx + \ . \ . \ . \ + Hx^{r-1})e^{ax} \cos \beta x \\ + (A_1 + B_1 x + \ . \ . \ . \ + H_1 x^{r-1})e^{ax} \sin \beta x,$$

containing, as it should, $2r$ arbitrary constants in all.

Example.

$$y^{\text{vi}} + m^2 y^{\text{iv}} - m^4 y'' - m^6 y = 0$$

$$(D^2 - m^2)(D^2 + m^2)^2 y = 0$$

$$y = (A + Bx) \cos mx + (A_1 + B_1 x) \sin mx + Ce^{mx} + C_1 e^{-mx}.$$

44. Inverse Operators. In preparation for the discussion of a particular integral of the non-reduced linear equation, we shall establish certain properties of the operator inverse to $F(D)$.

The operators $d()/dx$ and $\int()dx$ are inverses of one another; the former has been denoted by D, and it is natural to denote the latter by D^{-1} or $\frac{1}{D}$. This is justified by *

$$D^{-1}(Dy) = D(D^{-1}y) = y,$$

* Note that $\frac{y}{D}$ must not be written, as it is doubtful whether it means $\frac{1}{D}y$ or $y\frac{1}{D}$, and the operator is understood to have effect only on that which follows it.

indicating that the processes of integration and differentiation, successively performed, cancel one another. This is analogous to the relation between functions and their inverses; *e.g.* if exp denotes the exponential and log the natural logarithm,

$$\exp \log x = e^{\log x} = x,$$

a relation which holds identically, not for any particular x, and which justifies the symbolic relation

$$\exp \log = 1.$$

But a word of caution must be added. Since differentiation (D) is unambiguous, but integration (D^{-1}) is ambiguous, it may happen that if the integration is performed after the differentiation, an ambiguous element may remain. For example we have

$$D\{D^{-1}(2x+1)\} = D(x^2+x) = 2x+1,$$

justifying the statement $D \,.\, D^{-1} = 1$. But, on the other hand,

$$D^{-1}\{D(2x+1)\} = D^{-1}(2) = 2x + C,$$

where C is an arbitrary constant, so that the statement $D^{-1} \,.\, D = 1$ is subject to the qualification that the constant which D^{-1} introduces has been properly chosen.

Just as D^r indicates the operation of r-ple differentiation, so D^{-r} will indicate r-fold integration. This is a process which has a clear meaning, and the relations $D^r(D^{-r}) = 1$ and $D^{-r}(D^r) = 1$ are true, the former invariably, the latter subject to the proper choice of the coefficients in the polynomial of degree $r-1$ introduced by the integration. But the operator inverse to the polynomial differential operator $F(D)$ has not yet been identified with any manipulative process, and can be interpreted only in special cases which will now be considered.

We recall the relation (40.1)

$$F(D) \,.\, e^{ax}X = e^{ax}F(D+a)X.$$

Now $F(D+a)X$ is a function of x, say Y, dependent upon X, *i.e.*

$$F(D) \,.\, e^{ax}X = e^{ax}Y, \quad \text{where} \quad Y = F(D+a)X.$$

Thus $e^{ax}Y$ is obtained from $e^{ax}X$ by the operator $F(D)$; conversely $e^{ax}X$ may be obtained by applying the inverse operator on $e^{ax}Y$, or symbolically

$$e^{ax}X = \frac{1}{F(D)}\{e^{ax}Y\}.$$

By the same argument, since $F(D+a)X = Y$, we have

$$X = \frac{1}{F(D+a)}Y,$$

and so we have the important relation

$$\frac{1}{F(D)}\{e^{ax}Y\} = e^{ax}\frac{1}{F(D+a)}Y, \quad . \quad . \quad (44.1)$$

and in particular

$$\frac{1}{(D-a)^r}\{e^{ax}Y\} = e^{ax}\frac{1}{D^r}Y. \quad . \quad . \quad (44.2)$$

In the case $X=1$ we deduce from the relation $F(D)e^{ax} = F(a)e^{ax}$ that

$$\frac{1}{F(D)}e^{ax} = \frac{e^{ax}}{F(a)}, \quad . \quad . \quad . \quad (44.3)$$

provided that $F(a) \neq 0$. This interprets the inverse operator $F^{-1}(D)$ with respect to the exponential function. The exceptional case $F(a)=0$ implies that $D-a$ is a factor of $F(D)$; let it be a factor repeated r times, and write

$$F(D) = G(D)(D-a)^r, \quad \text{where} \quad G(a) \neq 0.$$

Let $F(D)$ be compounded of any two polynomial operators $G(D)$, $H(D)$ and let

$$Y = F(D)X = H(D)G(D)X.$$

Then

$$\frac{1}{H(D)}Y=G(D)X, \qquad \frac{1}{G(D)H(D)}Y=X=\frac{1}{F(D)}Y,$$

that is the inverse operator $F^{-1}(D)$ is equivalent to the inverse operators $H^{-1}(D)$, $G^{-1}(D)$ applied in succession.

Thus when $F(D)=G(D)(D-a)^r$,

$$\frac{1}{F(D)}e^{ax}=\frac{1}{(D-a)^r}\left\{\frac{1}{G(D)}e^{ax}\right\}=\frac{1}{(D-a)^r}\frac{e^{ax}}{G(a)}.$$

Putting $Y=1$ in (44.1) and noting that by ordinary integration

$$\frac{1}{D}\,.\,1=x, \quad \frac{1}{D^2}\,.\,1=\frac{x^2}{2}, \quad \frac{1}{D^3}\,.\,1=\frac{x^3}{6}, \;.\;.\;., \quad \frac{1}{D^r}\,.\,1=\frac{x^r}{r!},$$

ignoring the arbitrary constant that enters at each step, we find that

$$\frac{1}{F(D)}e^{ax}=\frac{1}{(D-a)^rG(D)}e^{ax}=\frac{e^{ax}x^r}{r!G(a)}. \qquad . \quad (44.4)$$

Thus we have shown that

(i) a particular integral of $F(D)y=e^{ax}$ is $y=e^{ax}/F(a)$ provided $F(a)\neq 0$.

(ii) when $F(D)$ is of the form $G(D)(D-a)^r$, where $G(a)\neq 0$, or when the auxiliary equation has a as an r-ple root, the simplest particular integral is $e^{ax}x^r/\{r!G(a)\}$.

Example 1.

$$y''+y'-6y=8e^{3x}.$$

Auxiliary equation :

$$r^2+r-6=0, \qquad \text{roots } r=2, \; -3.$$

Complementary function :

$$u=Ae^{2x}+Be^{-3x}$$

This does not contain a term in e^{3x}, so that a particular integral is

$$y=(D^2+D-6)^{-1}(8e^{3x})$$
$$=8e^{3x}/(3^2+3-6)=\tfrac{4}{3}e^{3x}.$$

General Integral:

$$y=Ae^{2x}+Be^{-3x}+\tfrac{4}{3}e^{3x}.$$

Note. When a particular integral satisfying certain specified conditions is required, it may be deduced from the general integral by assigning the proper values to the constants introduced by the complementary function. The number of independent conditions imposed cannot exceed the number of disposable constants which is given by the order of the equation.

For example, to determine the particular solution in Ex. 1 such that $y=0$, $y'=3$ when $x=0$. We have

$$y=Ae^{2x}+Be^{-3x}+\tfrac{4}{3}e^{3x}, \qquad y'=2Ae^{2x}-3Be^{-3x}+4e^{3x};$$

hence

$$0=A+B+\tfrac{4}{3}, \qquad 3=2A-3B+4.$$

Solving, we have $A=-1$, $B=-\tfrac{1}{3}$, and the particular integral satisfying the condition imposed is

$$y=\tfrac{4}{3}e^{3x}-e^{2x}-\tfrac{1}{3}e^{-3x}.$$

Example 2. Solution of

$$y''-3y'+2y=e^x+e^{2x}$$

such that $y=y'=1$ when $x=0$.

Complementary function $u=Ae^x+Be^{2x}$. This contains both terms of the right-hand side of the equation, *i.e.* $F(a)=0$ in both cases.

For a particular integral

$$y=(D-2)^{-1}(D-1)^{-1}(e^x+e^{2x}).$$

Taking the exponentials separately, substitute the coefficient of x for D in the non-critical factor only, thus:

$$y=-(D-1)^{-1}e^x+(D-2)^{-1}e^{2x}$$
$$=-e^xD^{-1}.1+e^{2x}D^{-1}.1=-xe^x+xe^{2x}.$$

Hence the general integral

$$y=(A-x)e^x+(B+x)e^{2x}.$$

To obtain the particular integral, make the required substitutions in this and in

$$y' = (A - 1 - x)e^{x} + (2B + 1 + 2x)e^{2x},$$

obtaining

$$1 = A + B, \quad 1 = A + 2B, \qquad \text{whence} \qquad A = 1, \quad B = 0.$$

The required particular integral therefore is

$$y = (1 - x)e^{x} + xe^{2x}.$$

45. Inverse Operators Relative to a Periodic Function. Equations of the form $F(D)y = \sin(mx + \epsilon)$ are of sufficient importance in applied mathematics to deserve special mention. We separate $F(D)$ into its even and odd parts, $F(D) = G(D^2) + DH(D^2)$. Then since

$$\begin{aligned} F(D) \sin(mx + \epsilon) &= \{G(D^2) + DH(D^2)\} \sin(mx + \epsilon) \\ &= \{G(-m^2) + DH(-m^2)\} \sin(mx + \epsilon) \\ &= (g + hD) \sin(mx + \epsilon), \end{aligned}$$

where g and h are constants, we conclude that, if $g \neq 0$, $h \neq 0$,

$$\frac{1}{F(D)} \sin(mx + \epsilon) = \frac{1}{g + hD} \sin(mx + \epsilon).$$

To evaluate this expression, we proceed as follows :—

$$\begin{aligned} \frac{1}{F(D)} \sin(mx + \epsilon) &= \frac{g - hD}{g^2 - h^2D^2} \sin(mx + \epsilon) \\ &= \frac{g - hD}{g^2 + h^2m^2} \sin(mx + \epsilon) \\ &= \frac{g \sin(mx + \epsilon) - hm \cos(mx + \epsilon)}{g^2 + h^2m^2} \\ &= \frac{\cos \epsilon_1 \sin(mx + \epsilon) - \sin \epsilon_1 \cos(mx + \epsilon)}{\sqrt{(g^2 + h^2m^2)}} \\ &= \frac{\sin(mx + \epsilon - \epsilon_1)}{\sqrt{(g^2 + h^2m^2)}}, \quad \text{where} \quad \tan \epsilon_1 = \frac{hm}{g}. \end{aligned}$$

Alternatively sines and cosines may be replaced by imaginary exponentials. Since $e^{i\theta}=\cos\theta+i\sin\theta$ we write $\cos\theta=\mathrm{R}e^{i\theta}$, $\sin\theta=\mathrm{I}e^{i\theta}$, where R denotes the real part, and I the coefficient of i in the imaginary part of $e^{i\theta}$. The above equation can therefore be written $F(D)y=\mathrm{I}e^{i(mx+\epsilon)}$. We shall, however, drop the symbol I for the time being and consider

$$F(D)y=e^{i(mx+\epsilon)}; \quad . \quad . \quad . \quad (45.1)$$

the coefficients in $F(D)$ are still supposed to be real, but y will now be an imaginary function of the real variable x.

Following the methods of § 44 we find that

$$y=\frac{1}{F(D)}e^{i(mx+\epsilon)}=\frac{e^{i(mx+\epsilon)}}{F(im)}.$$

But since

$$F(im)=G(-m^2)+imH(-m^2)=g+imh,$$

we have

$$y=\frac{e^{i(mx+\epsilon)}}{g+imh}=\frac{g-imh}{g^2+m^2h^2}e^{i(mx+\epsilon)}$$

or

$$\begin{aligned}(g^2+m^2h^2)y&=(g-imh)\{\cos(mx+\epsilon)+i\sin(mx+\epsilon)\}\\&=g\cos(mx+\epsilon)+mh\sin(mx+\epsilon)\\&\quad+i\{g\sin(mx+\epsilon)-mh\cos(mx+\epsilon)\}.\end{aligned}$$

This furnishes a particular integral of (45.1); taking in turn the imaginary and the real components we see that

$$y=\frac{g\sin(mx+\epsilon)-mh\cos(mx+\epsilon)}{g^2+m^2h^2}=\frac{\sin(mx+\epsilon-\epsilon_1)}{\sqrt{(g^2+m^2h^2)}}$$

is a particular integral of $F(D)y=\sin(mx+\epsilon)$, and

$$y=\frac{g\cos(mx+\epsilon)+mh\sin(mx+\epsilon)}{g^2+m^2+h^2}=\frac{\cos(mx+\epsilon-\epsilon_1)}{\sqrt{(g^2+m^2h^2)}}$$

is a particular integral of $F(D)y=\cos(mx+\epsilon)$.

Example 1. *Differential Equation for a simple Electric Circuit.* If i (amperes) is the current intensity * at time t (seconds) in a circuit containing inductance L (henries), resistance R (ohms) and capacity C (farads), under an impressed electromotive force e (volts), we have the differential equation

$$L\frac{d^2i}{dt^2}+R\frac{di}{dt}+\frac{i}{C}=\frac{de}{dt}.$$

A particular solution of the reduced equation is ϵ^{rt}, where

$$r=-\frac{R}{2L}\left\{1\pm\sqrt{\left(1-\frac{4L}{R^2C}\right)}\right\}$$

and three cases are possible:

(i) If $R^2C > 4L$, the radical is real but numerically less than unity; hence the complementary function is of the form $A\epsilon^{-at}+B\epsilon^{-bt}$, where a and b are real and positive.

(ii) If $R^2C=4L$, the complementary function has the form $\epsilon^{-at}(A+Bt)$, where $a=R/2L$ and is positive.

(iii) If $R^2C > 4L$ the radical is imaginary; the complementary function takes the form $\epsilon^{-at}(A\cos bt+B\sin bt)$, where a is positive.

In all three cases, the exponential rapidly becomes small, in fact negligible in practice, so that the complementary function represents a *transient* effect.

The most important form of e consists of a sum of sinusoidal terms; as their effect is additive we confine our attention to a single term

$$e=E\sin(\omega t+a)$$

when a particular integral of the differential equation is given by

$$i=\frac{CD}{CLD^2+CRD+1}E\sin(\omega t+a).$$

* Electrical engineers use the symbols i for current intensity and e for e.m.f.; they write j and ϵ in place of the conventional mathematical symbols i and e.

Evaluating this expression by the above method, we find

$$i=\frac{CE\omega}{\sqrt{\{(1-CL\omega^2)^2+(CR\omega)^2\}}}\sin(\omega t+a+\tfrac{1}{2}\pi-\beta),$$

where $\tan\beta=CR\omega/(1-CL\omega^2)$.

This gives the *steady-state* or permanent current, whose phase is behind that of the e.m.f. by the angle $90°-\beta$.

Example 2.

$$y''+m^2y=a\cos mx+b\sin mx,$$

where a and b are given constants. This is a case where the right-hand member is contained in the complementary function. If we take the equation

$$y''+m^2y=e^{imx},$$

we have the particular integral (*cf.* 44.4)

$$y=\frac{1}{D^2+m^2}e^{imx}=\frac{e^{imx}}{2im}x$$

$$=\frac{x}{2m}(\sin mx-i\cos mx).$$

Taking real and imaginary parts in turn we see that particular integrals of

$$y''+m^2y=\cos mx,\qquad y''+m^2y=\sin mx$$

are respectively

$$y=\frac{x}{2m}\sin mx,\qquad y=-\frac{x}{2m}\cos mx,$$

and a particular integral of the proposed equation is

$$y=\frac{x}{2m}(a\sin mx-b\cos mx).$$

46. Development of an Inverse Operator. Let the polynomial operator $F(D)$, with constant coefficients, contain the factors $D-a$ repeated r times, $D-\beta$ repeated s times and so on. Then we may write

$$\frac{1}{F(D)}=\frac{A_1}{D-a}+\frac{A_2}{(D-a)^2}+\ldots+\frac{A_r}{(D-a)^r}+\frac{B_1}{D-\beta}+\ldots,\qquad(46.1)$$

for if we operate on both members by $F(D)$ the left-hand becomes 1; the right-hand becomes a polynomial in D which will reduce to 1 if the constants $A_1, A_2, \ldots,$ $A_r, B_1 \ldots$ are determined just as they would be if the right-hand member were the algebraic development of the left-hand in partial fractions.

We may now interpret $(D-a)^{-1} . x^\kappa$, where κ is a positive integer, as

$$-\frac{1}{a}\left(1-\frac{D}{a}\right)^{-1}x^\kappa = -\frac{1}{a}\left\{1+\frac{D}{a}+\left(\frac{D}{a}\right)^2+\ldots+\left(\frac{D}{a}\right)^\kappa\right\}x^\kappa$$
$$= -\frac{1}{a}\left\{x^\kappa+\frac{\kappa}{a}x^{\kappa-1}+\frac{\kappa(\kappa-1)}{a^2}x^{\kappa-2}+\ldots+\frac{\kappa!}{a^\kappa}\right\},$$

for if we operate on the right-hand member by $D-a$ we recover x^κ. In similar fashion we can interpret $(D-a)^{-2}x^\kappa$ as

$$\frac{1}{a^2}\left(1-\frac{D}{a}\right)^{-2}x^\kappa = \frac{1}{a^2}\left\{1+\frac{2D}{a}+\frac{3D^2}{a^2}+\ldots+\frac{(\kappa+1)D^\kappa}{a^\kappa}\right\}x^\kappa$$

and expanding each term of (46.1) as a series of ascending powers of D, we arrive at the following interpretation of $F^{-1}(D)x^\kappa$:

$$F^{-1}(D)x^\kappa = (c_0+c_1D+c_2D^2+\ldots+c_\kappa D^\kappa)x^\kappa, \quad (46.2)$$

where the series on the right contains the first $\kappa+1$ terms of the algebraic development of $1/F(D)$ in ascending powers of D. It terminates in D^κ since $D^r x^\kappa = 0$ for $r > \kappa$. It follows that if $P(x)$ is a polynomial of degree κ,

$$F^{-1}(D) . P(x) = (c_0+c_1D+c_2D^2+\ldots+c_\kappa D^\kappa)P(x). \quad (46.3)$$

Example. Particular integral of

$$y''-7y'+12y = e^{2x}(x^3-5x^2)$$

$$\begin{aligned}
y &= (3-D)^{-1}(4-D)^{-1} . e^{2x}(x^3-5x^2)\\
&= e^{2x}(1-D)^{-1}(2-D)^{-1}(x^3-5x^2)\\
&= \tfrac{1}{2}e^{2x}(1+D+D^2+D^3)(1+\tfrac{1}{2}D+\tfrac{1}{4}D^2+\tfrac{1}{8}D^3)(x^3-5x^2)\\
&= e^{2x}(\tfrac{1}{2}+\tfrac{3}{4}D+\tfrac{7}{8}D^2+\tfrac{15}{16}D^3)(x^3-5x^2)\\
&= e^{2x}(\tfrac{1}{2}x^3+\tfrac{9}{4}x^2+\tfrac{21}{4}x+\tfrac{45}{8}-\tfrac{5}{2}x^2-\tfrac{15}{2}x-\tfrac{35}{4})\\
&= e^{2x}(\tfrac{1}{2}x^3-\tfrac{1}{4}x^2-\tfrac{9}{4}x-\tfrac{25}{8}).
\end{aligned}$$

47. General Integral by Quadratures. When the factors of $F(D)$ are distinct, the equation $F(D)y=f(x)$ may be integrated completely by quadratures. For we have

$$\frac{1}{F(D)}\cdot f(x)=\left\{\frac{1}{F'(\alpha)(D-\alpha)}+\frac{1}{F'(\beta)(D-\beta)}+\ .\ .\ .\right\}f(x).$$

Now

$$\frac{1}{D-\alpha}\cdot f(x)=\frac{1}{D-\alpha}\cdot e^{\alpha x}\{e^{-\alpha x}f(x)\}$$

$$=e^{\alpha x}\frac{1}{D}\{e^{-\alpha x}f(x)\}=e^{\alpha x}\left\{\int e^{-\alpha x}f(x)dx+C_1\right\}.$$

The general integral therefore is

$$y=\frac{e^{\alpha x}}{F'(\alpha)}\left\{\int e^{-\alpha x}f(x)dx+C_1\right\}+\frac{e^{\beta x}}{F'(\beta)}\left\{\int e^{-\beta x}f(x)dx+C_2\right\}+\ .\ .\ . \quad (47.1)$$

or it may be expressed in the form

$$y=\frac{1}{F'(\alpha)}\int_{x_1}^{x}e^{\alpha(x-t)}f(t)dt+\frac{1}{F'(\beta)}\int_{x_2}^{x}e^{\beta(x-t)}f(t)dt+\ .\ .\ ., \quad (47.2)$$

where the lower terminals x_1, x_2, . . . are arbitrary, or again as

$$y=u(x)+\int^{x}\left\{\frac{e^{\alpha(x-t)}}{F'(\alpha)}+\frac{e^{(\beta x-t)}}{F'(\beta)}+\ .\ .\ .\right\}f(t)dt, \quad (47.3)$$

where $u\ (x)$ is the complementary function, and the lower terminal of integration (which would merely lead to terms already existing in $u(x)$) is ignored.

If $D-\alpha$ is a double factor, let $F(D)=(D-\alpha)^2G(D)$. Then

$$\frac{1}{F(D)}\cdot f(x)=\left\{\frac{1}{G(\alpha)(D-\alpha)^2}-\frac{G'(\alpha)}{\{G(\alpha)\}^2(D-\alpha)}+\ .\ .\ .\right\}f(x).$$

Now

$$\frac{1}{(D-\alpha)^2}\cdot f(x)=e^{\alpha x}\frac{1}{D^2}\{e^{-\alpha x}f(x)\}=e^{\alpha x}\{\textstyle\iint e^{-\alpha x}f(x)dx^2+C_1x+C_2\}.$$

Thus a double factor leads to a double integral and in general an r-fold factor to an r-fold integral.

Example. Particular integral of

$$y'' + a^2y = e^{\mu x} \cos ax$$

$$y = \frac{1}{D^2 + a^2} e^{\mu x} \cos ax = \frac{1}{2ai}\left\{\frac{1}{D - ai} - \frac{1}{D + ai}\right\} e^{\mu x} \cos ax$$

$$= \frac{1}{2ai}\int^x \{e^{ai(x-t)} - e^{-ai(x-t)}\} e^{\mu t} \cos at \, dt$$

$$= \frac{1}{a}\int^x \sin a(x-t) e^{\mu t} \cos at dt$$

$$= \frac{1}{2a}\int^x e^{\mu t}\{\sin ax + \sin (ax - 2at)\} dt$$

$$= \frac{1}{2a\mu} e^{\mu x} \sin ax + \frac{1}{2a(\mu^2 + 4a^2)} e^{\mu x}\{2a \cos ax - \mu \sin ax\}$$

$$= \frac{1}{\mu^2 + 4a^2} e^{\mu x}\left\{\cos ax + \frac{2a}{\mu} \sin ax\right\}.$$

48. The Euler Linear Equation.

$$x^n \frac{d^n y}{dx^n} + a_1 x^{n-1} \frac{d^{n-1}y}{dx^{n-1}} + \; . \; . \; . \; + a_{n-1} x \frac{dy}{dx} + a_n y = f(x). \quad (48.1)$$

This equation may be reduced to one with constant coefficients by the substitution $x = e^t$. For

$$\frac{dy}{dx} = \frac{dy}{dt} \cdot \frac{dt}{dx} = \frac{1}{x}\frac{dy}{dt}; \qquad \frac{d^2y}{dx^2} = \frac{1}{x^2}\frac{d^2y}{dt^2} - \frac{1}{x^2}\frac{dy}{dt},$$

and in general, if D now represents $d()/dt$,

$$x^r \frac{d^r y}{dx^r} = D(D-1) \; . \; . \; . \; (D - r + 1)y,$$

and the transformed equation can be rearranged as

$$(D^n + A_1 D^{n-1} + \; . \; . \; . \; + A_{n-1} D + A_n) y = f(e^t) \quad (48.2)$$

whose constant coefficients $A_1, \ldots, A_n$ can be expressed linearly in terms of $a_1, \ldots, a_n$.

Alternatively we may introduce a new operator ϑ:

$$x\frac{dy}{dx}=\vartheta y, \qquad x^2\frac{d^2y}{dx^2}=\vartheta(\vartheta-1)y, \ldots,$$

$$x^r\frac{d^ry}{dx^r}=\vartheta(\vartheta-1)\ldots(\vartheta-r+1)y$$

so that the transformed equation is

$$(\vartheta^n+A_1\vartheta^{n-1}+\ldots+A_{n-1}\vartheta+A_n)y=f(x) \qquad (48.3)$$

whose coefficients are identical with those of (48.2).

Taking as basis the fact that the operators $\vartheta-\alpha$ and $\vartheta-\beta$ are permutable when α, β are constants, we may establish a calculus of the polynomial operator $F(\vartheta)$ and of its inverse $F^{-1}(\vartheta)$ similar to that of $F(D)$ and its inverse. In particular

$$F(\vartheta)x^r=F(r)x^r, \qquad F(\vartheta)x^rX=x^rF(\vartheta+r)X,$$

where X is a function of x, and conversely,

$$F^{-1}(\vartheta)x^r=x^r/F(r) \quad \text{provided } F(r)\neq 0, \qquad (48.4)$$

$$F^{-1}(\vartheta)x^rX=x^rF^{-1}(\vartheta+r)X. \qquad (48.5)$$

If $\quad F(\vartheta)=(\vartheta-r)^aG(\vartheta),$

then

$$\begin{aligned}F^{-1}(\vartheta)x^r&=(\vartheta-r)^{-a}G^{-1}(\vartheta)x^r\\&=(\vartheta-r)^{-a}x^r/G(r)=x^r\vartheta^{-a}(1)/G(r).\end{aligned}$$

But since

$$\vartheta y=xdy/dx, \qquad \vartheta^{-1}y=\int ydx/x.$$

Hence

$$\vartheta^{-1}(1)=\int dx/x=\log|x|$$

$$\vartheta^{-2}(1)=\int\log|x|\,dx/x=\tfrac{1}{2}(\log|x|)^2,$$

and in general

$$\vartheta^{-a}(1)=(\log|x|)^a/a\,!$$

The complementary function will contain terms like Cx^r, where r is a root of the *indicial equation*

$$r^n+A_1r^{n-1}+\ldots+A_{n-1}r+A_n=0.$$

If this equation has n distinct roots, $r=\alpha, \beta, \ldots, \kappa$ the complete complementary function will be

$$C_1x^\alpha + C_2x^\beta + \ldots + C_nx^\kappa.$$

In the case of a root $r=\alpha$ repeated s times, the complementary function will contain a corresponding group of terms

$$x^\alpha\{C_1 + C_2 \log |x| + \ldots + C_s(\log |x|)^{s-1}\}.$$

The most important type of non-reduced Euler linear equation is that in which $f(x)$ is composed of terms like x^m and $x^m(\log|x|)^k$. A particular integral may be obtained by the use of (48.4) and (48.5), or by assuming a method of undetermined coefficients (see Ex. 2 below).

An equation of the more general type

$$(ax+b)^n\frac{d^ny}{dx^n} + a_1(ax+b)^{n-1}\frac{d^{n-1}y}{dx^{n-1}} + \ldots + a_{n-1}(ax+b)\frac{dy}{dx} + a_ny = f(x)$$

may be brought into the above form by the linear substitution $ax+b=\xi$, or it may be transformed immediately into an equation with constant coefficients by writing $ax+b=e^t$. The indicial equation is found by substituting $(ax+b)^r$ in the reduced equation and proceeding as above.

Example 1.

$$x^2y'' - 2xy' + 2y = x + x^2 \log|x| + x^3.$$

In terms of the operator ϑ the left-hand member is

$$\vartheta(\vartheta-1)y - 2\vartheta y + 2y = (\vartheta^2 - 3\vartheta + 2)y = (\vartheta-1)(\vartheta-2)y.$$

The complementary function therefore is $Ax + Bx^2$.

The separate contribution of each of the three terms on the right of the equation may be found as follows:—

$$(\vartheta-1)^{-1}(\vartheta-2)^{-1}x = x\vartheta^{-1}(\vartheta-1)^{-1}\,.\,1 = -x\vartheta^{-1}\,.\,1 = -x\log|x|$$

$$(\vartheta-1)^{-1}(\vartheta-2)^{-1}x^2\log|x|$$
$$= x^2(\vartheta+1)^{-1}\vartheta^{-1}\,.\,\log|x| = x^2(1-\vartheta)\vartheta^{-1}\,.\,\log|x|$$
$$= x^2(\vartheta^{-1}-1)\log|x| = x^2\{\tfrac{1}{2}(\log|x|)^2 - \log|x|\}$$

$$(\vartheta-1)^{-1}(\vartheta-2)^{-1}x^3 = (2)^{-1}(1)^{-1}x^3 = \tfrac{1}{2}x^3.$$

The general integral therefore is

$$y = Ax + Bx^2 - x \log | x | + x^2\{\tfrac{1}{2}(\log | x |)^2 - \log | x |\} + \tfrac{1}{2}x^3.$$

Example 2.

$$(2x+1)^2 y'' + (4x+2)y' - 4y = x^2.$$

Substituting $(2x+1)^r$ in the reduced equation, we get

$$4r(r-1) + 4r - 4 = 0 \quad \text{or} \quad r^2 - 1 = 0.$$

Hence the complementary function

$$A(2x+1) + B(2x+1)^{-1}.$$

As $x^2 = \frac{1}{4}(2x+1)^2 - \frac{1}{2}(2x+1) + \frac{1}{4}$ and $2x+1$ occurs in the complementary function, a particular integral of the form

$$y = a(2x+1)^2 + b(2x+1) \log | 2x+1 | + c$$

may be assumed. Substituting we find that

$$12a(2x+1)^2 + 8b(2x+1) - 4c = x^2,$$

whence

$$a = \tfrac{1}{48}, \qquad b = -\tfrac{1}{16}, \qquad c = -\tfrac{1}{16}.$$

49. The Laplace Linear Equation. In this equation the coefficients are linear functions of the independent variable, thus:

$$(a_0 + b_0 x)y^{(n)} + (a_1 + b_1 x)y^{(n-1)} + \ldots + (a_n + b_n x)y = 0. \qquad (49.1)$$

If the constants b were all zero, the solution would be of exponential form. It was probably this consideration that suggested the possibility of satisfying the equation by an integral of the form

$$I = \int e^{xt} f(t)dt \quad . \quad . \quad . \quad (49.2)$$

in which $f(t)$ and a range of integration *independent of* x are at our disposal. We have in general

$$d^r I/dx^r = \int e^{xt} t^r f(t)dt,$$

so that if Ly represents the left-hand member of (49.1), we have

$$LI = \int e^{xt}\{(a_0 + b_0 x)t^n + (a_1 + b_1 x)t^{n-1} + \ldots + a_n + b_n x\}f(t)dt$$
$$= \int e^{xt}\{P(t) + xQ(t)\}f(t)dt,$$

where

$$P(t)=a_0t^n+a_1t^{n-1}+\ .\ .\ .\ +a_n,$$
$$Q(t)=b_0t^n+b_1t^{n-1}+\ .\ .\ .\ +b_n.$$

Now

$$\int e^{xt}xQ(t)f(t)dt=\int Q(t)f(t)\frac{\partial}{\partial t}(e^{xt})dt=[e^{xt}Q(t)f(t)]-\int e^{xt}\frac{d}{dt}\{Q(t)f(t)\}dt.$$

Thus $LI=0$ if

(i) $f(t)$ is such that

$$\frac{d}{dt}\{Q(t)f(t)\}-P(t)f(t)=0;$$

(ii) $f(t)$ having been determined, the range of integration is such that

$$[e^{xt}Q(t)f(t)]=0$$

independently of x. The former condition is satisfied by

$$f(t)=\frac{1}{Q(t)}\exp\left\{\int\frac{P(t)}{Q(t)}dt\right\}\quad .\quad .\quad (49.3)$$

and the latter becomes

$$[e^{xt+\int(P/Q)dt}]=0.\quad .\quad .\quad .\quad (49.4)$$

Note. It is often advantageous to replace t in (49.2) by a constant multiple as $-t$ or it.

Example.

$$xy''+(2n+1)y'+xy=0.$$

In this case

$$P(t)=(2n+1)t,\qquad Q(t)=t^2+1,$$
$$\int(P/Q)dt=\log(t^2+1)^{n+\frac{1}{2}};\qquad f(t)=(t^2+1)^{n-\frac{1}{2}}.$$

Then, replacing t by it,

$$I=\int e^{ixt}(1-t^2)^{n-\frac{1}{2}}dt$$

satisfies the differential equation provided that I is convergent and that the terminals are so chosen that

$$[e^{ixt}(1-t^2)^{n+\frac{1}{2}}]=0$$

identically. The former condition is satisfied if n is positive; the latter if the range of integration is $(-1, +1)$. The imaginary part of the integral vanishes; taking the real part we conclude that the equation is satisfied by

$$y=\int_{-1}^{1} \cos(xt)(1-t^2)^{n-\frac{1}{2}}dt.$$

Writing $t=\cos\theta$ we find that an equivalent solution is

$$y=\int_0^{\pi} \cos(x\cos\theta)\sin^{2n}\theta\, d\theta,$$

an integral well known in the theory of Bessel functions.

50. Variation of Parameters. When the complementary function of any linear equation

$$y^{(n)}+p_1y^{(n-1)}+\ldots+p_{n-1}y'+p_ny=f(x) \qquad (50.1)$$

is known, the complete solution may be obtained by quadratures as follows. If the complementary function is

$$u=C_1u_1+\ldots+C_nu_n$$

we replace the constants C by symbols V representing functions of x, thus

$$y=V_1u_1+\ldots+V_nu_n.$$

These n symbols are at our disposal, so we proceed to set up n linear relations between the derivatives $V_1', \ldots, V_n'$. First of all we have

$$y'=V_1u_1'+\ldots+V_nu_n'$$

provided that

$$V_1'u_1+\ldots+V_n'u_n=0. \qquad (50.2)$$

Then

$$y''=V_1u_1''+\ldots+V_nu_n''$$

provided that

$$V_1'u_1'+\ldots+V_n'u_n'=0, \qquad (50.3)$$

and we continue up to the stage

$$y^{(n-1)}=V_1u_1^{(n-1)}+\ldots+V_nu_n^{(n-1)}$$

provided that

$$V_1'u_1^{(n-2)} + \ldots + V_n'u_n^{(n-2)} = 0. \qquad (50.4)$$

Thus $n-1$ linear homogeneous relations have been established between $V_1', \ldots, V_n'$. If we substitute the above expressions for $y, y', \ldots, y^{(n-1)}$ in (50.1), and also substitute for $y^{(n)}$ its value

$$V_1u_1^{(n)} + \ldots + V_nu_n^{(n)} + V_1'u_1^{(n-1)} + \ldots + V_n'u_n^{(n-1)}$$

we shall find that

$$V_1'u_1^{(n-1)} + \ldots + V_n'u_n^{(n-1)} = f(x). \qquad (50.5)$$

This is the final relation between $V_1', \ldots, V_n'$; we solve the system algebraically and obtain $V_1, \ldots, V_n$ by quadratures, thus obtaining a complete solution of the equation.

In the case of the equation of the second order

$$y'' + py' + qy = r, \qquad (50.6)$$

if u_1, u_2 are the constituents of the complementary function, we write $y = V_1u_1 + V_2u_2$ and determine V_1', V_2' by the relations

$$V_1'u_1 + V_2'u_2 = 0, \qquad V_1'u_1' + V_2'u_2' = r.$$

If $W = u_1u_2' - u_1'u_2$ we have

$$WV_1' = -ru_2, \qquad WV_2' = ru_1,$$

so that the general integral is

$$y = -u_1\int\frac{ru_2}{W}dx + u_2\int\frac{ru_1}{W}dx. \qquad (50.7)$$

Example.

$$y'' + y = \sec x.$$

With the above notation we have

$$y = V_1 \cos x + V_2 \sin x, \qquad W = 1.$$

Hence

$$y = -\cos x\int \sec x \sin x\, dx + \sin x\int \sec x \cos x\, dx$$
$$= (A + \log|\cos x|)\cos x + (B + x)\sin x.$$

51. Linear Systems with Constant Coefficients. By introducing a new variable t upon which x and y are dependent, the linear fractional equation (17.3) may be replaced by a system of two linear equations

$$\frac{dx}{dt}=lx+my, \qquad \frac{dy}{dt}=ax+by. \quad . \quad . \tag{51.1}$$

This system will be satisfied by $x=Ae^{rt}$, $y=A_1e^{rt}$ if

$$(l-r)A+mA_1=0, \qquad aA+(b-r)A_1=0.$$

Eliminating A, A_1 we have the characteristic equation

$$(l-r)(b-r)-am=0 \quad \text{or} \quad r^2-(b+l)r+bl-am=0.$$

If this equation has two distinct roots (real or complex) α and β, the general solution of the system is

$$x=Ae^{\alpha t}+Be^{\beta t}, \qquad my=(\alpha-l)Ae^{\alpha t}+(\beta-l)Be^{\beta t}, \tag{51.2}$$

dependent therefore upon two arbitrary constants A, B.

When $r=\alpha$ is a double root, we take, by analogy with the linear equation with constant coefficients, a tentative solution

$$x=e^{\alpha t}(At+B), \qquad y=e^{\alpha t}(A_1t+B_1).$$

On substitution we find that

$$(l-\alpha)A+mA_1=0, \qquad aA+(b-\alpha)A_1=0,$$
$$(l-\alpha)B+mB_1=A, \qquad aB+(b-\alpha)B_1=A_1,$$

whence

$$x=e^{\alpha t}(At+B), \qquad my=e^{\alpha t}\{(\alpha-l)At+(\alpha-l)B+A\}. \quad . \tag{51.3}$$

We may regard (51.2) or (51.3), as the case may be, as a parametric general integral of the linear fractional equation.

An alternative method is to eliminate all of the dependent variables but one, which will be illustrated by the system of three homogeneous equations

$$\left.\begin{aligned} L_1x + L_2y + L_3z = 0 \\ M_1x + M_2y + M_3z = 0 \\ N_1x + N_2y + N_3z = 0 \end{aligned}\right\}, \qquad (51.4)$$

where the 9 coefficients L_1 to N_3 represent polynomials in the operator $d()/dt$ with constant coefficients. It will be supposed that the system is determinate, which implies that the determinant Δ of the coefficients is not zero. This determinant itself will, in general, be a polynomial in $d()/dt$; its degree is the *order* of the system.

By operating on the left-hand members of (51.4) by the minors of L_1, M_1, N_1 respectively, we obtain $\Delta x = 0$. Similarly, $\Delta y = 0$, $\Delta z = 0$. Thus x, y, z are particular integrals of the reduced linear equation $\Delta u = 0$, whose order is that of the system, provided always that Δ is not a mere constant, in which case the only possible solution would be $x = y = z = 0$.

Setting this case aside, x, y, z will be of the forms

$$\begin{aligned} x &= P_1e^{\alpha t} + Q_1e^{\beta t} + \ldots, \\ y &= P_2e^{\alpha t} + Q_2e^{\beta t} + \ldots, \\ z &= P_3e^{\alpha t} + Q_3e^{\beta t} + \ldots, \end{aligned}$$

where α, β, . . . are the distinct roots of the characteristic equation $\Delta(r) = 0$, where P_1, P_2, P_3 are polynomials of degree $s - 1$ in t, if s is the multiplicity of the root α, and similarly for the rest. By substitution in (51.4) we establish relationships between each group of three polynomials, whereby their coefficients become dependent upon a limited number from among them. It is possible to show that the number of constants finally remaining arbitrary is equal to the order of the system.

By exactly the same process, a system

$$\left.\begin{aligned} L_1x + M_1y + N_1z = f_1(t) \\ L_2x + M_2y + N_2z = f_2(t) \\ L_3x + M_3y + N_3z = f_3(t) \end{aligned}\right\} \qquad (51.5)$$

is transformed into

$$\Delta x = g_1(t), \qquad \Delta y = g_2(t), \qquad \Delta z = g_3(t). \quad . \ (51.6)$$

If $x = X$, $y = Y$, $z = Z$ is the complete solution of the corresponding reduced system (51.4) and if a particular solution of (51.5) is $x = \phi_1$, $y = \phi_2$, $z = \phi_3$, the general solution of the system will be

$$x = X + \phi_1, \qquad y = Y + \phi_2, \qquad z = Z + \phi_3.$$

Example 1.

$$\frac{dx}{dt} = x - 2y, \qquad \frac{dy}{dt} = 5x + 3y.$$

The characteristic equation of the system is

$$\begin{vmatrix} 1 - r & -2 \\ 5 & 3 - r \end{vmatrix} = 0$$

or $r^2 - 4r + 13 = 0$, whence $r = 2 \pm 3i$. Substituting

$$x = e^{2t}(A \cos 3t + B \sin 3t), \qquad y = e^{2t}(A_1 \cos 3t + B_1 \sin 3t)$$

in the system, we obtain the four consistent equations

$$\begin{aligned} A + 3B &= -2A_1, & 3A - B &= 2B_1, \\ A_1 - 3B_1 &= -5A, & 3A_1 + B_1 &= -5B, \end{aligned}$$

and thus the general solution is

$$\begin{aligned} x &= e^{2t}(A \cos 3t + B \sin 3t), \\ y &= \tfrac{1}{2}e^{2t}\{-(A + 3B) \cos 3t + (3A - B) \sin 3t\}. \end{aligned}$$

Example 2.

$$\begin{cases} D(D+1)x + D(D^2 + D - 1)y + (D - 1)z = e^t \\ Dx + (D^2 - 1)y - z = 0 \\ x + Dy + Dz = 0 \end{cases}$$

where $D = d()/dt$. By elimination, we obtain

$$(D - 1)^2 x = -e^t, \qquad (D - 1)^2 y = 2e^t, \qquad (D - 1)^2 z = -e^t,$$

whence

$$x = e^t(At + B - \tfrac{1}{2}t^2), \quad y = e^t(A_1 t + B_1 + t^2), \quad z = e^t(A_2 t + B_2 - \tfrac{1}{2}t^2).$$

On substituting for x, y, z we obtain the six consistent equations

$$2A+A_1=-4, \qquad 3A+2B+4A_1+B_1+A_2=-6,$$
$$A-A_2=-3, \qquad A+B+2A_1-B_2=-2,$$
$$A+A_1+A_2=-1, \qquad B+A_1+B_1+A_2+B_2=0,$$

giving

$$A_1=-2A-4, \qquad A_2=A+3,$$
$$B_1=4A-2B+7, \qquad B_2=-3A+B-6.$$

Hence the general integral is

$$x=e^t(At+B-\tfrac{1}{2}t^2), \qquad y=e^t\{-(2A+4)t+4A-2B+7+t^2\}.$$
$$z=e^t\{(A+3)t-3A+B-6-\tfrac{1}{2}t^2\}.$$

The system is thus of the second order.

CHAPTER VI

SOLUTION IN SERIES

52. Solution Developed as a Taylor Series. We consider a linear equation of the second order

$$\frac{d^2y}{dx^2}=p(x)\frac{dy}{dx}+q(x)y. \quad . \quad . \quad . \quad (52.1)$$

in which we shall regard x as a complex variable.

This type includes many equations of very great importance which cannot be solved in terms of simple combinations of elementary functions. Given such an equation, the usual procedure is to express the solution (which may be a solution satisfying certain initial conditions) in the form of an infinite series from which tables of the value of the solution may, if desired, be computed. Thus the convergence of the series is important, not only as a basis of the validity of the process, but also as an indication of the practical value of the result, for a slowly converging series is of little use to a computer.

It will be assumed that the coefficients $p(x)$, $q(x)$ are one-valued, and have derivatives of all orders except possibly for certain isolated values of x. Let $x=a$ be a value for which p, q and all derivatives are finite : we shall obtain a solution such that y and y' have assigned finite values y_0, y_0' when $x=a$.

By substituting in (52.1) we obtain the corresponding value of the second derivative, namely

$$y_0''=p(a)y_0'+q(a)y_0.$$

Differentiating (52.1), we obtain

$$y''' = p(x)y'' + \{p'(x) + q(x)\}y' + q'(x)y,$$

and as y_0, y_0', y_0'' are known, y_0''' can be obtained immediately. Continuing the process, we obtain the values of successive derivatives for $x=a$, and thus we have the coefficients in the Taylor series

$$y = y_0 + y_0'(x-a) + y_0''\frac{(x-a)^2}{2\,!} + \ldots + y_0^{(n)}\frac{(x-a)^n}{n\,!} + \ldots$$

Borrowing from the language of the theory of functions of a complex variable, a point $x=a$ at which the above conditions are satisfied is said to be an *ordinary point* of the equation.

Example 1. To find the solution of

$$y'' + xy = 0$$

such that $y=A$, $y'=B$ when $x=0$.

We have

$$y'' = -xy, \qquad y''' = -xy' - y, \qquad y^{\text{iv}} = -xy'' - 2y',$$

and in general

$$y^{(n)} = -xy^{(n-2)} - (n-2)y^{(n-3)}.$$

The origin is an ordinary point; putting $x=0$ in the above, we have

$$y_0'' = 0, \qquad y_0''' = -y_0, \qquad y_0^{\text{iv}} = -2y_0', \qquad y^{\text{v}} = -3y_0'' = 0,$$

and in general

$$y_0^{(n)} = -(n-2)y_0^{(n-3)}.$$

We thus find that

$$y_0^{(3n)} = (-1)(-4)(-7)\ \ldots\ (-3n+2)A,$$

$$y_0^{(3n+1)} = (-2)(-5)(-8)\ \ldots\ (-3n+1)B, \qquad y_0^{(3n+2)} = 0.$$

Thus the required solution is

$$y = A\left(1 - \frac{x^3}{3\,!} + \frac{4x^6}{6\,!} - \frac{28x^9}{9\,!} + \ldots\right) + B\left(x - \frac{2x^4}{4\,!} + \frac{10x^7}{7\,!} - \frac{80x^{10}}{10\,!} + \ldots\right),$$

and it may be verified that (i) the ratio test proves the convergence of each series for all values of x, (ii) each series separately satisfies the differential equation. Since A and B may be regarded as arbitrary constants, the above is an expression of the general solution.

Note 1. When $p(x)$, $q(x)$ are polynomials of low degree, a more practical way of obtaining the solution is to assume a series of ascending powers of x

$$y = c_0 + c_1 x + c_2 x^2 + \ldots = \Sigma c_r x^r,$$

to substitute this series in the differential equation and to determine the coefficients so that the equation is identically satisfied; that is to say, so that the coefficient of each individual power of x cancels out.

Example 2.

$$y'' - xy' + ny = 0.$$

Substituting the above series in the left-hand member and equating to zero the coefficients of successive powers of x in the result, we obtain the following set of *recurrence relations* :—

$$2c_2 + nc_0 = 0, \qquad 6c_3 + (n-1)c_1 = 0,$$
$$12c_4 + (n-2)c_2 = 0, \qquad 20c_5 + (n-3)c_3 = 0,$$

and in general, by equating to zero the coefficient of x^r,

$$(r+1)(r+2)c_{r+2} + (n-r)c_r = 0 \qquad (r = 0, 1, 2, \ldots).$$

We see that the coefficients of even rank (*i.e.* suffix) depend on c_0 but not on c_1; those of odd rank on c_1 but not on c_0, and that c_0, c_1 are arbitrary. Denoting by $S_1(x)$ the series obtained by taking $c_0 = 1$, $c_1 = 0$ and by $S_2(x)$ that obtained by assuming $c_0 = 0$, $c_1 = 1$, we have

$$S_1(x) = 1 - \frac{n}{2\,!}x^2 + \frac{n(n-2)}{4\,!}x^4 - \frac{n(n-2)(n-4)}{6\,!}x^6 + \ldots$$

$$S_2(x) = x - \frac{n-1}{3\,!}x^3 + \frac{(n-1)(n-3)}{5\,!}x^5 - \frac{(n-1)(n-3)(n-5)}{7\,!}x^7 + \ldots$$

Since

$$\frac{c_{r+2}}{c_r} = \frac{r-n}{(r+1)(r+2)} \to 0 \qquad \text{as } r \to \infty$$

for any finite value of n, both series converge for all values of x. The general integral is $y = AS_1(x) + BS_2(x)$, where A, B are arbitrary constants. It will be noted that when n is an even positive integer the series S_1 terminates and reduces to a polynomial of degree n; where n is odd, S_2 is a polynomial of degree n.

Note 2. It is sometimes possible, by a change of dependent variable, to simplify a linear equation, or to identify it with one previously studied. The transformation most frequently employed is of the form

$$y = uv,$$

where y is the original, v the new dependent variable, and u a chosen function of x.

For example, if the equation

$$y'' + (n + \tfrac{1}{2} - \tfrac{1}{4}x^2)y = 0$$

is satisfied by a series of ascending integral powers of x as in the preceding example, the recurrence relation between the coefficients is

$$(r+1)(r+2)c_{r+2} + (n + \tfrac{1}{2})c_r - \tfrac{1}{4}c_{r-2} = 0.$$

This is a three-term recurrence relation which is much more difficult to manipulate than one that involves only two terms. If, however, we make the substitution

$$y = e^{-\frac{1}{4}x^2}v,$$

so that

$$y'' = e^{-\frac{1}{4}x^2}\{v'' - xv' + (\tfrac{1}{4}x^2 - \tfrac{1}{2})v\},$$

we find that the equation in v is

$$v'' - xv' + nv = 0,$$

which is precisely the equation considered above.

53. Regular Singularity. When we consider an equation of the form

$$P(x)y'' + Q(x)y' + R(x)y = 0 \quad . \quad . \quad (53.1)$$

we see that if $x - a$ is a factor of the coefficient $P(x)$, but not of both $Q(x)$ and $R(x)$, the equation fails to determine a value of y'' for $x = a$, and the procedure of § 52 is inapplicable. We then say that $x = a$ is a *singular point* or *singularity* of the equation.

The form of a solution valid in the neighbourhood of a singularity may therefore differ from that of a solution appropriate to an ordinary point. It is important to investigate this difference, which is not merely a matter of theoretical interest, but of practical importance, as the solutions valid in the neighbourhood of singular points are as a general rule those required in physical applications.

We find a clue to a fruitful line of approach in the equation

$$(x-a)^2y''+b(x-a)y'+cy=0,$$

where b and c are constants. This equation has (§ 48) a solution of the form $y=(x-a)^\sigma$, so that the singularity of the equation may imply a singularity (*e.g.* a pole or a branch-point) in its solution. When (53.1) can be written in the form

$$(x-a)^2P_1(x)y''+(x-a)Q_1(x)y'+R_1(x)y=0,$$

such that $P_1(a)\neq 0$ and $P_1(x)$, $Q_1(x)$, $R_1(x)$ are finite in the neighbourhood of $x=a$, it is thus natural to assume a solution of the form

$$y=(x-a)^\sigma F(x),$$

where $F(x)$ is a function which can be developed as a Taylor series in $x-a$. It will be found on substitution, equating to zero the lowest power of $x-a$, that σ is determined by the *indicial equation* of the second degree

$$\sigma(\sigma-1)P_1(a)+\sigma Q_1(a)+R_1(a)=0,$$

giving in general two distinct values of σ and leading to two distinct solutions. Such a singularity is termed *regular*.

54. The Hypergeometric Equation. This is the equation

$$x(1-x)y''+\{\gamma-(\alpha+\beta+1)x\}y'-\alpha\beta y=0, \qquad (54.1)$$

in which α, β, γ are constants, at present unrestricted. On multiplying the equation throughout by x, it will be seen that $x=0$ is a regular singularity; similarly, the singularity $x=1$ is regular, and there are no other finite singularities.

Confining our attention to the singularity $x=0$, we assume the series

$$c_0x^\sigma + c_1x^{\sigma+1} + \ldots + c_rx^{\sigma+r} + \ldots \quad (c_0 \neq 0), \qquad (54.2)$$

in which the index σ is, for the moment, regarded as an arbitrary parameter, and denote it by $\phi(x, \sigma)$. Denoting the left-hand member of the equation by Ly, we find on substituting $\phi(x, \sigma)$ for y and arranging the terms in ascending powers of x, that

$$Ly = \sigma(\sigma-1+\gamma)c_0x^{\sigma-1}$$
$$+\sum_{r=0}^{\infty}\{(\sigma+r+1)(\sigma+r+\gamma)c_{r+1} - (\sigma+r+\alpha)(\sigma+r+\beta)c_r\}x^{\sigma+r}.$$

If now, whatever σ may be, we choose the coefficients $c_1, c_2, \ldots$ so that

$$(\sigma+r+1)(\sigma+r+\gamma)c_{r+1} = (\sigma+r+\alpha)(\sigma+r+\beta)c_r \quad (r \geqslant 0) \qquad (54.3)$$

leaving c_0 arbitrary, we find that

$$c_1 = \frac{(\sigma+\alpha)(\sigma+\beta)}{(\sigma+1)(\sigma+\gamma)}c_0, \quad c_2 = \frac{(\sigma+\alpha)(\sigma+\alpha+1)(\sigma+\beta)(\sigma+\beta+1)}{(\sigma+1)(\sigma+2)(\sigma+\gamma)(\sigma+\gamma+1)}c_0,$$

and so on, and these coefficients are finite provided that neither σ nor $\sigma+\gamma-1$ is a negative integer. Setting such cases aside, we have proved that if

$$\phi(x, \sigma) =$$
$$c_0x^\sigma\left\{1+\sum_{r=1}^{\infty}\frac{(\sigma+\alpha)\ldots(\sigma+\alpha+r-1)(\sigma+\beta)\ldots(\sigma+\beta+r-1)}{(\sigma+1)\ldots(\sigma+r)(\sigma+\gamma)\ldots(\sigma+\gamma+r-1)}x^r\right\}$$

and if the series is convergent, then

$$L\phi(x, \sigma) = \sigma(\sigma-1+\gamma)c_0x^{\sigma-1}.$$

The question of convergence can be settled once and for all by the ratio test, for

$$\frac{c_{r+1}}{c_r} = \frac{(\sigma + r + a)(\sigma + r + \beta)}{(\sigma + r + 1)(\sigma + r + \gamma)} \to 1 \quad \text{as } r \to \infty,$$

σ, a, β, γ being finite, and so the series converges for $|x| < 1$.

We can make $L\phi(x, \sigma) = 0$, and thus satisfy the equation, by taking

$$\sigma(\sigma - 1 + \gamma) = 0 \quad . \quad . \quad . \quad (54.4)$$

provided that the stipulation that neither σ nor $\sigma + \gamma - 1$ is a negative integer is not violated. Thus the roots of the indicial equation are $\sigma = 0$ provided $\gamma - 1$ is not a negative integer, and $1 - \gamma$ provided $1 - \gamma$ is not a negative integer.

Take first the index $\sigma = 0$. A solution is provided by

$$\phi(x, 0) =$$

$$c_0\left\{1 + \sum \frac{a(a+1) \ldots (a+r-1)\beta(\beta+1) \ldots (\beta+r-1)}{r!\,\gamma(\gamma+1) \ldots (\gamma+r-1)} x^r\right\}$$

provided that γ is not zero or a negative integer. Next take the alternative index $\sigma = 1 - \gamma$, which gives $\phi(x, 1-\gamma) = c_0 x^{1-\gamma}$

$$\times\left\{1 + \sum \frac{(a-\gamma+1) \ldots (a-\gamma+r)(\beta-\gamma+1) \ldots (\beta-\gamma+r)}{(2-\gamma) \ldots (r+1-\gamma)r!} x^r\right\}$$

provided γ is not a positive integer greater than unity.

When $\gamma = 1$ the two particular solutions are identical. We shall suppose that γ is not an integer, positive or negative, or zero and use the notation

$$F(a, \beta;\, \gamma;\, x) = 1 + \frac{a \,.\, \beta}{1 \,.\, \gamma} x + \frac{a(a+1)\beta(\beta+1)}{2!\,\gamma(\gamma+1)} + \ldots$$

for the *hypergeometric series*. Writing A and B for c_0 and c_1 respectively, we may express the general solution of the hypergeometric equation as

$$y=AF(\alpha,\ \beta\ ;\ \gamma\ ;\ x)+Bx^{1-\gamma}F(\alpha-\gamma+1,\ \beta-\gamma+1\ ;\ 2-\gamma\ ;\ x).$$

The above procedure is known as the *Method of Frobenius.*

Note 1. It is possible by a modification of the above procedure to obtain the complete solution when γ has one of the excluded values, but the results are not of any particular interest. The essential feature is that the solution that becomes irrelevant is replaced by one involving logarithmic terms. This point will be illustrated later in the case of the Legendre equation.

Note 2. The general solution valid in the neighbourhood of the singularity $x=1$ is

$$y=AF(\alpha,\ \beta\ ;\ \alpha+\beta-\gamma+1\ ;\ 1-x)$$
$$+B(1-x)^{\gamma-\alpha-\beta}F(\gamma-\alpha,\ \gamma-\beta\ ;\ \gamma-\alpha-\beta+1\ :\ 1-x)$$

provided that $\alpha+\beta-\gamma$ is not an integer or zero.

55. The Legendre Equation and the Function $P_n(x)$. The equation

$$(1-x^2)y''-2xy'+n(n+1)y=0\ . \qquad . \ (55.1)$$

has the finite regular singularities $x=\pm 1$; in order to study the solutions valid near $x=1$ it is advantageous to make the change of variable $x=1-2\xi$, which transforms the equation into

$$\xi(1-\xi)\frac{d^2y}{d\xi^2}+(1-2\xi)\frac{dy}{d\xi}+n(n+1)y=0.$$

This is the particular case of the hypergeometric equation in which $\alpha=n+1$, $\beta=-n$, $\gamma=1$; in fact it is a case in which the two fundamental solutions corresponding to (54.4) become identical, and we are left with

$$y=F(n+1,\ -n\ ;\ 1\ ;\ \xi).$$

The corresponding solution of the Legendre equation, or *Legendre Function of the First Kind*, is defined as

$$P_n(x)=F(n+1,\ -n;\ 1;\ \tfrac{1}{2}-\tfrac{1}{2}x).$$

We shall confine our attention to the important case in which n is a positive integer; since the term in ξ^{n+1} and every succeeding term in the hypergeometric series $F(\alpha,\ \beta;\ \gamma;\ \xi)$ contains the factor $\beta+n$, it is clear that $F(n+1,\ -n;\ 1;\ \xi)$ is a polynomial in ξ of degree n. Hence

$$P_n(x)=1-\frac{n(n+1)}{1}\frac{1-x}{2}+\frac{(n-1)n(n+1)(n+2)}{(2\,!)^2}\left(\frac{1-x}{2}\right)^2+\dots$$
$$\dots+(-)^n\frac{1\,.\,2\,.\,.\,.\,(n-1)n(n+1)\,.\,.\,.\,2n}{(n\,!)^2}\left(\frac{1-x}{2}\right)^n$$

is a polynomial in x of degree n such that $P_n(1)=1$. In particular,

$$P_0(x)=1,\quad P_1(x)=x,\quad P_2(x)=\tfrac{1}{2}(3x^2-1),\quad P_3(x)=\tfrac{1}{2}(5x^3-3x).$$

The final term in the above expression for $P_n(x)$ is the only term that gives rise to x^n; we see therefore that the coefficient of x^n is $(2n)\,!/2^n(n\,!)^2$. The whole expression may be expanded and then rearranged in descending powers of x, but it is less laborious to substitute the polynomial

$$y=c_0+c_1x+c_2x^2+\dots+c_nx^n=\Sigma c_rx^r$$

in the left-hand member of (55.1) and to equate the coefficient of each power of x to zero. Taking the coefficient of x^{r-2} we have

$$r(r-1)c_r=(r+n-1)(r-n-2)c_{r-2}.$$

As c_n is known, we work backwards and find

$$c_{n-2}=-\frac{n(n-1)}{2(2n-1)}c_n,\qquad c_{n-4}=\frac{n(n-1)(n-2)(n-3)}{2\,.\,4(2n-1)(2n-3)}c_n,$$

$$c_{n-2r}=(-)^r\frac{n(n-1)\,.\,.\,.\,(n-2r+1)}{2^r\,r!\,(2n-1)(2n-3)\,.\,.\,.\,(2n-2r+1)}c_n.$$

It is easily verified that the coefficient of x^{n-1} in the expansion of $P_n(x)$ is zero, from which it follows in succession that $c_{n-3}, c_{n-5}, \ldots$ are zero. Hence

$$P_n(x) = \frac{(2n)!}{2^n(n!)^2}\left\{x^n - \frac{n(n-1)}{2(2n-1)}x^{n-2} + \frac{n(n-1)(n-2)(n-3)}{2.4.(2n-1)(2n-3)}x^{n-4} - \ldots\right\}$$

$$= \sum_{r=0}^{N}(-)^r \frac{(2n-2r)!}{2^n\, r!\,(n-r)!\,(n-2r)!}x^{n-2r},$$

where $N = \frac{1}{2}n$ for n even, $N = \frac{1}{2}(n-1)$ for n odd.

Thus the *Legendre polynomial* $P_n(x)$ is even or odd according as its degree n is even or odd; since $P_n(1) = 1$, we conclude that $P_n(-1) = (-1)^n$.

Note. An important formula for $P_n(x)$ may be deduced from this last expansion. We observe that

$$\frac{(2n-2r)!}{(n-2r)!}x^{n-2r} = \frac{d^n}{dx^n}x^{2n-2r}$$

and therefore

$$P_n(x) = \frac{d^n}{dx^n}\sum \frac{(-)^r x^{2n-2r}}{2^n r!(n-r)!}$$

where r ranges originally from 0 to N. We may extend the range of summation, however, from $r=0$ to $r=n$, for the new terms of the sum are of degree less than n and their n^{th} derivatives vanish. Thus we can employ the Binomial Theorem and obtain the *Rodrigues Formula*

$$P_n(x) = \frac{1}{2^n . n!}\frac{d^n}{dx^n}(x^2-1)^n.$$

We may prove from this formula that $P_n(x)$ has n distinct zeros between -1 and 1. Let $f_0 = (x^2-1)^n$, $f_m = f'_{m-1}$ for $m = 1, 2, \ldots, n$, so that $f_n = 2^n n!\, P_n(x)$. Then we prove by induction that f_m has at least m distinct zeros in $(-1, 1)$. For this is true of f_0; further, f_{m-1} has zeros at -1 and 1 and so, if it has at least $m-1$ distinct zeros in $(-1, 1)$, then by Rolle's theorem f_m has at least m distinct zeros there. The induction now proceeds.

56. Solution for Large Values of $|x|$. Physical problems not infrequently demand the solution of a linear differential equation for large positive or large negative values of the argument x. In such cases we use the reciprocal transformation $x=1/\xi$ whereby (53.1) becomes

$$P(\xi^{-1})\left\{\xi^4\frac{d^2y}{d\xi^2}+2\xi^3\frac{dy}{d\xi}\right\}+Q(\xi^{-1})\left\{-\xi^2\frac{dy}{d\xi}\right\}+R(\xi^{-1})y=0,$$

retaining its linear form. The point $x=\infty$ is said to be ordinary or singular according as $\xi=0$ is an ordinary or singular point of this transformed equation.

The Legendre equation, so transformed, becomes

$$(1-\xi^{-2})\left\{\xi^4\frac{d^2y}{d\xi^2}+2\xi^3\frac{dy}{d\xi}\right\}-2\xi^{-1}\left\{-\xi^2\frac{dy}{d\xi}\right\}+n(n+1)y=0$$

or

$$L_\xi y=\xi^2(\xi^2-1)\frac{d^2y}{d\xi^2}+2\xi^3\frac{dy}{d\xi}+n(n+1)y=0.$$

Assuming

$$y=\Sigma c_r\xi^{\sigma+r} \qquad (c_0\neq 0)$$

we find that

$$L_\xi y=c_0(\sigma+n)(\sigma-n-1)\xi^\sigma$$

provided that $c_1\, c_2,\ .\ .\ .$ are so chosen that

$$(\sigma+r-n+1)(\sigma+r+n+2)c_{r+2}=(\sigma+r)(\sigma+r+1)c_r \quad (r\geqslant 0).$$

The equation is thus satisfied if $\sigma=-n$ or $n+1$; when $\sigma=-n$ the solution is of the form

$$y=c_0\xi^{-n}+c_2\xi^{-n+2}+c_4\xi^{-n+4}\ .\ .\ .$$

with the recurrence-relation

$$(r+2)(2n-r-1)c_{r+2}=-(n-r)(n-r-1)c_r.$$

Reverting to the variable x we have the first solution

$$y_1=c_0\left\{x^n-\frac{n(n-1)}{2(2n-1)}x^{n-2}+\frac{n(n-1)(n-2)(n-3)}{2\,.\,4(2n-1)(2n-3)}x^{n-4}-\ .\ .\ .\right\}$$

and taking $c_0=(2n)!\,/2^n(n!)^2$ when n is a positive integer we identify this solution with the polynomial $P_n(x)$.

When $\sigma=n+1$ the solution is

$$y=c_0\xi^{n+1}+c_2\xi^{n+3}+c_4\xi^{n+5}+\ldots,$$

with the recurrence-relation

$$(r+2)(2n+r+3)c_{r+2}=(n+r+1)(n+r+2)c_r.$$

Thus we obtain the second solution

$$y_2=c_0\left\{x^{-n-1}+\frac{(n+1)(n+2)}{2(2n+3)}x^{-n-3}\right.$$
$$\left.+\frac{(n+1)(n+2)(n+3)(n+4)}{2\,.\,4(2n+3)(2n+5)}x^{-n-5}+\ldots\right\}$$

When n is a positive integer this series does not terminate, but since

$$\frac{c_{r+2}}{c_r}=\frac{(n+r+1)(n+r+2)}{(r+2)(2n+r+3)}\to 1 \quad \text{as } r\to\infty,$$

it converges for $|x|>1$. Taking $c_0=2^n(n\,!)^2/(2n+1)\,!$ we obtain the second solution

$$Q_n(x)=\sum_{r=0}^{\infty}\frac{2^n(n+r)\,!\,(n+2r)\,!}{r\,!\,(2n+2r+1)\,!}x^{-n-2r-1}$$

which is known as the Legendre Function of the Second Kind. It is of opposite parity to $P_n(x)$.

Note. The method explained in § 38 enables us to determine a second solution by quadrature. Substituting in (55.1)

$$y=P_n(x)\int v\,dx$$

we find for v the differential equation

$$2P_n'/P_n-\frac{2x}{1-x^2}+\frac{v'}{v}=0,$$

from which

$$v=C(1-x^2)^{-1}\{P_n(x)\}^2.$$

Thus we have a second solution of Legendre's equation in the form

$$P_n(x)\int\frac{dx}{(1-x^2)\{P_n(x)\}^2}.$$

It is possible to prove that this is equal to $Q_n(x)$, provided that the lower limit of integration is taken at infinity.

57. The Bessel Equation and the Function $J_n(x)$. Unlike the Legendre equation, the Bessel equation

$$x^2y'' + xy' + (x^2 - n^2)y = 0 \quad . \quad . \quad (58.1)$$

is not essentially a particular case of the hypergeometric equation. It has only the one finite singularity $x=0$, which is regular ; the point at infinity is also a singularity, but is irregular.

To obtain a solution in series by the Frobenius method, write Ly for the left-hand member of the equation and

$$\phi(x, \sigma) = \sum c_r x^{\sigma+r} \qquad (c_0 \neq 0).$$

Then

$$L\phi(x, \sigma) = c_0(\sigma^2 - n^2(x^\sigma + c_1\{(\sigma+1)^2 - n^2\}x^{\sigma+1},$$

provided the coefficients $c_2, c_3, \ldots, c_r, \ldots$ are such that

$$\{(\sigma+r)^2 - n^2\}c_r + c_{r-2} = 0 \qquad (r \geqslant 2).$$

If $y=\phi(x, \sigma)$ is a solution, $L\phi(x, \sigma)$ must vanish identically, and therefore

$$c_0(\sigma^2 - n^2) = 0, \qquad c_1\{(\sigma+1)^2 - n^2\} = 0.$$

Since $c_0 \neq 0$ we must take $\sigma = \pm n$ and consequently $c_1 = 0$. The relation between c_r and c_{r-2} now shows, taking $r=3, 5, \ldots$ in succession, that all coefficients of odd rank vanish.

Taking first of all $\sigma = n$ and writing $r = 2s$ we have

$$4s(n+s)c_{2s} = -c_{2s-2} \qquad (s \geqslant 1)$$

and thus we obtain the solution

$$y = \phi(x, n) = c_0\left\{x^n - \frac{x^{n+2}}{2^2(n+1)} + \ldots + \frac{(-)^s x^{n+2s}}{2^{2s}(n+1)\ldots(n+s) \, . \, s!} + \ldots\right\}.$$

The coefficients are finite except when n is a negative integer. Excluding this case, we standardise the solution by taking $c_0 = 1/2^n\Gamma(n+1)$ in general and $c_0 = 1/2^n n\,!$ when n is a positive integer. Since

$$\frac{c_{2s}}{c_{2s-2}} = -\frac{1}{4s(n+s)} \to 0 \quad \text{as } s \to \infty,$$

the series converges for any finite value of x, and thus we have the first solution $y = J_n(x)$, where

$$J_n(x) = \sum_{s=0}^{\infty} \frac{(-)^s}{s\,!\,\Gamma(n+s+1)} \left(\frac{x}{2}\right)^{n+2s}$$

in general. In particular, when n is a positive integer,

$$J_n(x) = \sum \frac{(-)^s}{s\,!\,(n+s)\,!} \left(\frac{x}{2}\right)^{n+2s}.$$

This function $J_n(x)$ is known as the *Bessel Function of the First Kind* of order n.

When n is not an integer the second solution may be obtained by replacing n by $-n$; it is therefore

$$J_{-n}(x) = \sum_{s=0}^{\infty} \frac{(-)^s}{s\,!\,\Gamma(s-n+1)} \left(\frac{x}{2}\right)^{2s-n}.$$

The leading terms of $J_n(x)$ and $J_{-n}(x)$ are respectively finite (non-zero) multiples of x^n and x^{-n}; the one is not a mere multiple of the other and therefore the general solution of the Bessel equation may be expressed as

$$y = AJ_n(x) + BJ_{-n}(x).$$

But when n is an integer, and since n appears in the differential equation only as n^2 there is no loss of generality in taking it to be a positive integer, $J_{-n}(x)$ is not distinct from $J_n(x)$. For the denominators of the first n terms of the series for $J_{-n}(x)$ contain respectively the factors $\Gamma(1-n)$, $\Gamma(2-n)$, . . ., $\Gamma(0)$ which are infinite, and so these terms vanish. Thus

$$J_{-n}(x)=\sum_{s=n}^{\infty}\frac{(-)^s}{s!\,\Gamma(s-n+1)}\left(\frac{x}{2}\right)^{2s-n}$$

$$=\sum_{r=0}^{\infty}\frac{(-)^{r+n}}{(r+n)!\,\Gamma(r+1)}\left(\frac{x}{2}\right)^{2r+n}=(-)^n J_n(x).$$

In this case a modification of the method of Frobenius is necessary to give an independent second solution.

58. The Function $Y_n(x)$. Consider the functions

$$J_{n+\epsilon}(x)=\sum\frac{(-)^s}{s!\,\Gamma(s+n+\epsilon+1)}\left(\frac{x}{2}\right)^{2s+n+\epsilon},$$

$$J_{-n-\epsilon}(x)=\sum\frac{(-)^s}{s!\,\Gamma(s-n-\epsilon+1)}\left(\frac{x}{2}\right)^{2s-n-\epsilon},$$

where n is a positive integer and ϵ a real number numerically less than unity. Both satisfy the Bessel equation

$$x^2y''+xy'+\{x^2-(n+\epsilon)^2\}y=0$$

and so does the function

$$\eta=\frac{J_{n+\epsilon}(x)-(-)^nJ_{-n-\epsilon}(x)}{\epsilon}.$$

So if $Ly\equiv x^2y''+xy'+(x^2-n^2)y$, then

$$L\eta=\{(n+\epsilon)^2-n^2\}\eta=\epsilon(2n+\epsilon)\eta.$$

If, therefore, η has a limit as $\epsilon\to 0$, $y=\lim\eta$ is a solution of $Ly=0$, *i.e.* is a Bessel function of order n. We prove that the limit exists by making the following transformation:

$$\lim_{\epsilon\to 0}\frac{J_{n+\epsilon}(x)-(-)^nJ_{-n-\epsilon}(x)}{\epsilon}$$

$$=\lim\left\{\frac{J_{n+\epsilon}(x)-J_n(x)}{\epsilon}+(-)^n\frac{J_{-n}(x)-J_{-n-\epsilon}(x)}{\epsilon}\right\}$$

$$=\left[\frac{\partial J_\nu(x)}{\partial\nu}-(-)^n\frac{\partial J_{-\nu}(x)}{\partial\nu}\right]_{\nu=n}$$

and evaluating these partial derivatives. Some authorities

take the latter expression to be the definition of the standard second solution $Y_n(x)$, but we shall follow the modern practice of introducing the factor π^{-1} and defining $Y_n(x)$ thus *

$$Y_n(x) = \frac{1}{\pi}\left[\frac{\partial J_\nu(x)}{\partial \nu} - (-)^n \frac{\partial J_{-\nu}(x)}{\partial \nu}\right]_{\nu=n}.$$

Since

$$J_\nu(x) = \sum_{s=0}^{\infty} \frac{(-)^s}{s!\,\Gamma(s+\nu+1)}\left(\frac{x}{2}\right)^{2s+\nu}$$

we have

$$\frac{\partial J_\nu(x)}{\partial \nu} = \sum \frac{(-)^s}{s!\,\Gamma(s+\nu+1)}\left(\frac{x}{2}\right)^{2s+\nu} \{\log(\tfrac{1}{2}x) - \psi(s+\nu+1)\},$$

where $\psi(z) = \Gamma'(z)/\Gamma(z)$. Hence †

$$\left[\frac{\partial J_\nu(x)}{\partial \nu}\right]_{\nu=n} = \sum_{s=0}^{\infty} \frac{(-)^s}{s!\,(s+n)!}\left(\frac{x}{2}\right)^{2s+n}$$

$$\times\left\{\log(\tfrac{1}{2}x) + \gamma - 1 - \tfrac{1}{2} - \ldots - \frac{1}{s+n}\right\}$$

$$= J_n(x)\{\log(\tfrac{1}{2}x) + \gamma\} - \sum_{s=0}^{\infty} \frac{(-)^s}{s!\,(s+n)!}$$

$$\times\left(1 + \tfrac{1}{2} + \ldots + \frac{1}{s+n}\right)\left(\frac{x}{2}\right)^{2s+n}.$$

* This definition was adopted in the *British Association Mathematical Tables*, vol. vi (Cambridge, 1937). An equivalent definition is

$$Y_n(x) = \lim_{\nu \to n} \frac{J_\nu(x)\cos\nu\pi - J_{-\nu}(x)}{\sin\nu\pi}.$$

† Since $\Gamma(z+1) = z\Gamma(z)$, we have $\psi(z+1) = \psi(z) + 1/z$ and so when z is a positive integer,

$$\psi(z+1) = \psi(1) + 1 + \tfrac{1}{2} + \tfrac{1}{3} + \ldots + \frac{1}{z}$$

where $-\psi(1) = \gamma = 0{\cdot}57721566 \ldots$ (Euler's constant).

It will be remembered that the first n terms in $J_{-\nu}(x)$ vanish when $\nu=n$; we therefore write

$$J_{-\nu}(x)=\sum_{s=0}^{n-1}\frac{(-)^s}{s\,!\,\Gamma(s-\nu+1)}\left(\frac{x}{2}\right)^{2s-\nu}+\sum_{s=n}^{\infty}\frac{(-)^s}{s\,!\,\Gamma(s-\nu+1)}\left(\frac{x}{2}\right)^{2s-\nu}.$$

In the first sum we use the relation

$$\Gamma(z)\Gamma(1-z)=\pi/\sin z\pi \quad \text{with} \quad z=s-\nu+1;$$

in the second we replace s by $s+n$, and thus obtain

$$J_{-\nu}(x)=\sum_{s=0}^{n-1}\frac{(-)^s\sin(s-\nu+1)\pi\,.\,\Gamma(\nu-s)}{\pi\,.\,s\,!}\left(\frac{x}{2}\right)^{2s-\nu}$$

$$+\sum_{s=0}^{\infty}\frac{(-)^{s+n}}{(s+n)\,!\,\Gamma(s+n-\nu+1)}\left(\frac{x}{2}\right)^{2s+2n-\nu}.$$

Differentiating with respect to ν, we have

$$\frac{\partial J_{-\nu}(x)}{\partial\nu}=\sum_{s=0}^{n-1}\frac{(-)^s}{\pi\,.\,s\,!}\left(\frac{x}{2}\right)^{2s-\nu}\sin(s-\nu+1)\pi\,.\,\Gamma(\nu-s)$$

$$\times\left\{-\frac{\pi\cos(s-\nu+1)\pi}{\sin(s-\nu+1)\pi}+\psi(\nu-s)-\log\left(\frac{x}{2}\right)\right\}$$

$$+\sum_{s=0}^{\infty}\frac{(-)^{s+n}}{(s+n)\,!\,\Gamma(s+n-\nu+1)}\left(\frac{x}{2}\right)^{2s+2n-\nu}$$

$$\times\left\{\psi(s+n-\nu+1)-\log\left(\frac{x}{2}\right)\right\}$$

$$\left[\frac{\partial J_{-\nu}(x)}{\partial\nu}\right]_{\nu=n}=\sum_{s=0}^{n-1}\frac{(-)^s}{s\,!}\left(\frac{x}{2}\right)^{2s-n}\Gamma(n-s)\cos(s-n)\pi$$

$$+\sum_{s=0}^{\infty}\frac{(-)^{s+n}}{(s+n)\,!\,s\,!}\left(\frac{x}{2}\right)^{2s+n}\left\{\psi(s+1)-\log\left(\frac{x}{2}\right)\right\}$$

$$= (-)^n \sum_{s=0}^{n-1} \frac{(n-s-1)!}{s!}\left(\frac{x}{2}\right)^{2s-n} - \sum_{s=0}^{\infty} \frac{(-)^{s-n}}{s!\,(s+n)!}\left(\frac{x}{2}\right)^{2s+n}$$

$$\times \left\{\log\left(\frac{x}{2}\right) + \gamma - 1 - \tfrac{1}{2} - \ldots - \frac{1}{s}\right\}$$

$$= (-)^n \sum_{s=0}^{n-1} \frac{(n-s-1)!}{s!}\left(\frac{x}{2}\right)^{2s-n} - (-)^n J_n(x)\{\log(\tfrac{1}{2}x) + \gamma\}$$

$$+ (-1)^n \sum_{s=0}^{\infty} \frac{(-)^s}{s!\,(s+n)!}\left(1 + \tfrac{1}{2} + \ldots + \frac{1}{s}\right)\left(\frac{x}{2}\right)^{2s+n}.$$

Thus the function $Y_n(x)$ or *Bessel Function of the Second Kind* of order n is given by

$$\pi Y_n(x) = \left[\frac{\partial J_\nu(x)}{\partial \nu}\right]_{\nu=n} - (-)^n \left[\frac{\partial J_{-\nu}(x)}{\partial \nu}\right]_{\nu=n}$$

$$= 2J_n(x)\{\log(\tfrac{1}{2}x) + \gamma\} - \sum_{s=0}^{n-1} \frac{(n-s-1)!}{s!}\left(\frac{x}{2}\right)^{2s-n}$$

$$- \sum_{s=0}^{\infty} \frac{(-)^s}{s!\,(n+s)!}\left(1 + \tfrac{1}{2} + \ldots + \frac{1}{s} + 1 + \tfrac{1}{2} + \ldots + \frac{1}{n+s}\right)\left(\frac{x}{2}\right)^{n+2s}$$

and when n is a positive integer the complete solution of the Bessel equation is

$$y = AJ_n(x) + BY_n(x).$$

EXAMPLES

1. $(x^2 - x)y' = y^2 + y$
2. $xy' + y^2 = 1$
3. $(1 + y)y' = x^2(1 - y)$
4. $xy' + (2x^2 - 1)\cot y = 0$
5. $2xy(x + 1)y' = y^2 + 1$
6. $x\sqrt{(y^2 - 1)}dx + y\sqrt{(x^2 - 1)}dy = 0$
7. $\sqrt{(1 - x^2)}dy = (1 + y^2)dx$
8. $y' + (1 - y^2)\tan x = 0$
9. $x(1 - x^2)dy = (x^2 - x + 1)ydx$
10. $xy^3y' = 1 - x^2 + y^2 - x^2y^2$
11. $(x^2 + a^2)y' = (y + b)\{x + \sqrt{(x^2 + a^2)}\}$
12. $x^2(y + a)^2(y' - 1) = y^2 - 2ax^2y + a^2$
13. $(x^2 + y^2)y' = xy$
14. $(x^2 - 2xy - y^2)y' = x^2 + 2xy - y^2$
15. $(x^2 + 2xy)y' = y^2 - 2xy$
16. $x(x^2 - 6y^2)dy = 4y(x^2 + 3y^2)dx$
17. $y - xy' = \sqrt{(x^2 + y^2)}$
18. $x^2ydx - (x^3 + ay^3)dy = 0$
19. $x(x - ay)y' = y(y - ax)$
20. $(x^2 + xy + ay^2)y' = ax^2 + xy + y^2$
21. $x(x + y)dy = (x^2 + y^2)dx$
22. $x(x^2 + axy + y^2)y' = y(x^2 + bxy + y^2)$
23. $(x + y)^2y' = x^2 - 2xy + 5y^2$
24. $xy' = y - x\cos^2(y/x)$
25. $(3y - x)y' = 3x - y + 4$
26. $(x - 5y + 5)dx + (5x - y + 1)dy = 0$
27. $(4y + x)y' = y - 4x$
28. $(9x + 2y + 19)dy = (2x + 6y - 18)dx$
29. $(9x + 21y + 3)y' = 7x - 5y + 45$
30. $(8x + y + 25)dx + (7x - 16y + 140)dy = 0$
31. $(2x - 4y + 5)y' = x - 2y + 3$
32. $(y + ax + b)y' = y + ax - b$
33. $x^2y' = (2x - y + 1)^2$
34. $(x + y + a + b)^2y' = 2(y + a)^2$
35. $(x - y)^2y' = (x - y + 1)^2$
36. $(x + y)^2dy = (x + y + 2)^2dx$

Show that 37–44 are exact, and integrate them:

37. $(ax + hy)dx + (hx + by)dy = 0$
38. $(3x^2 + 4xy)dx + (2x^2 + 3y^2)dy = 0$
39. $\{3ax^2 + 2(a + 2h)xy + (b + 2h)y^2\}dx + \{(a + 2h)x^2 + 2(b + 2h)xy + 3by^2\}dy = 0$
40. $(4x^3y - 12x^2y^2 + 5x^2 + 3x)y' + 6x^2y^2 - 8xy^3 + 10xy + 3y = 0$
41. $x^2y'/y + 2x\log|y| = 0$
42. $(\cos x - x\cos y)dy - (\sin y + y\sin x)dx = 0$
43. $2\dfrac{x + a}{y + b}dx - \left(\dfrac{x + a}{y + b}\right)^2 dy = 0$
44. $\dfrac{(1 - y^2)dx + (1 - x^2)dy}{(1 + xy)^2} = 0$

Show that each of equations 45–56 has an integrating factor of one or other of the types $\mu(x)$, $\mu(y)$, $\mu(x+y)$, $\mu(xy)$, and hence integrate:

45. $(x+y)dx+dy=0$
46. $(x^3+y^4)dx+8xy^3dy=0$
47. $xy^3dx+(x^2y^2-1)dy=0$
48. $(1-xy)dx+(1-x^2)dy=0$
49. $y^2dx+(xy+1)dy=0$
50. $dx+\{1+(x+y)\tan y\}dy=0$
51. $(x^3-2y^3-3xy)dx+3x(y^2+x)dy=0$
52. $(x^2-y^2+1)dx+(x^2-y^2-1)dy=0$
53. $(2x^2+xy+a^2)ydx+(x+2y)(x^2+a^2)dy=0$
54. $(3x^5y^8-y^3)dx+(5x^6y^7+x^3)dy=0$
55. $(y+1)dx+(xy+y^2+y+1)dy=0$
56. $(7x^3+3x^2y+4y)dx+(4x^3+x+5y)dy=0$
57. $xy'-y=x^3+1$
58. $xy'+y=x\log|x|$
59. $(x+1)y'-y=3x^4+4x^3$
60. $(x^2+a)y'-xy=a$
61. $(1-x^2)y'-xy=1$
62. $(1-x^2)y'-y=1-x^2$
63. $(1+x^2)y'+xy=3x^3$
64. $(2xy'+y)\sqrt{(1+x)}=1+2x$
65. $\sqrt{(1+x^2)}y'+y=2x$
66. $2x(x-1)y'+(2x-1)y=x$
67. $x^2y'+xy=x^2+x+1$
68. $2(x^2+x+1)y'+(2x+1)y=8x^2+1$
69. $(x^2-1)y'-xy=x^2$
70. $x(1-x^2)y'+(2x^2-1)y=x^3-x^5$
71. $(1+x^2)y'+2xy=\tan x$
72. $2(1-x^2)y'-(1+x)y=\sqrt{(1-x^2)}$
73. $2(1-x)y'-y=4x\sqrt{(1-x)}$
74. $(1+x^2)^2y'+(1+x)(1+x^2)y=2x$
75. $xy'+2y=\sin x$
76. $y'\cos x+y\sin x-\cos^2 x=0$
77. $y'+y\tan x=\sin 2x$
78. $y'\sin x\cos^3 x+y\cos 2x\cos^2 x=1$
79. $y'+y\cos x=\frac{1}{2}\sin 2x$
80. $y'\sin x-y\cos x=e^x\sin^2 x$
81. $y'-y=x+\sin x$
82. $\frac{1}{2}y'=y\tan 2x+1+\sec 2x$
83. $y'+2y=x^2+3\cosh x$
84. $y'\cos x+y\sin x=1+\tan x$
85. $y'+y\tanh x=6e^{2x}$
86. $y'\sin^2 x-y\tan x=\tan x-\tan^3 x$
87. $y'\cos x-3y\sin x=\cot x$
88. $y'+2y\operatorname{cosec} 2x=2\cot^2 x\cos 2x$
89. $y'\tan x+y=\sin 3x+\operatorname{cosec} 2x$
90. $y'\cot x-y=\operatorname{cosec} 2x+\cos 2x$
91. $(1-x^2)y'+xy=x\arcsin x+(1-x)\sqrt{(1-x^2)}$
92. $x(x+1)y'-(x^2+x-1)y=(x+1)(x^2-1)$
93. $xy'=4y-4\sqrt{y}$
94. $2xy'-y=(2x^3-1)/y$
95. $xy'=y+2xy^2$
96. $(1+x^2)y'+xy=xy^2$
97. $x^3y'=2x^2y+y^3$
98. $xy'+y=y^2\log|x|$

99. $xy' + y = xy^3$ 100. $x^2y' + xy + \sqrt{y} = 0$
101. $3xy' - 2y = xy^4$ 102. $y' \cos x + y \sin x + y^3 = 0$
103. $y' + 2y = 2xy^{3/2}$ 104. $2(1+x)yy' + 2x - 3x^2 + y^2 = 0$

Equation 105 has a particular solution $y = 1$, 106 has $y = (x+1)/x^2$, and 107–110 have $y = x$; complete the integration:

105. $y' = (y-1)(xy - y - x)$ 106. $y' + y^2 = x^{-4}$
107. $xy' + (m-1)ax^m(y-x)^2 + y - 2x = 0$
108. $y' + xy^2 - (2x^2+1)y + x^3 + x - 1 = 0$
109. $(x^2 + a)y' + 2y^2 - 3xy - a = 0$
110. $2x^2y' = 2xy + (y^2 - x^2)(x \cot x - 1)$

Integrate 111–118 by means of a change of variable:

111. $x(y'+1) + \tan(x+y) = 0$ 112. $xy' - y = x^2 + y^2$
113. $(1-x^2)yy' + xy^2 + 2x^2 = 0$
114. $2(1+x)yy' + y^2 + 2x - 3x^2 = 0$
115. $(x^2 + xy + 1)y' = (y^2 + xy + 1)$
116. $(x^2 + y^2 - a)yy' + x(x^2 + y^2 + a) = 0$
117. $\{(x^2 + y^2 - a)x - y\}y' = (x^2 + y^2 - a)y + x$
118. $(x^2 + y^2 - a)(x + yy') = 2xy(y - xy')$
119. $(x^2 - y^4)y' = xy$ [Substitute $x = ty$]
120. $(xy' - 2y)^2 = x^2(x^4 - y^2)$ [Substitute $y = tx^2$]
121. $(x^4 - 1)(xy' - y) = 2x(y^2 - x^2)$ [Substitute $y = tx$]
122. Substitute $y = x(1+z)/(1-z)$ in $x^m(xy' - y) = y^2 - x^2$. Hence integrate when (i) $m = 0$, (ii) $m = 1$, (iii) $m = 2$

Find the equations of families of curves having the following properties (123–132): 123. Radius vector equals tangent 124. Normal bisected by y-axis 125. Tangent has constant length a (Tractrix) 126. Area of trapezium bounded by axes, tangent and ordinate $= a^2$ 127. Projection of ordinate on normal $= a$ 128. Subtangent $\overline{NT}$ equals abscissa of projection of origin on tangent 129. Mid-point of normal lies on $y^2 = ax$ 130. Ordinate NP meets $y = ax + b$ in Q; R is taken on NP so that $\overline{PR} = \overline{NQ}$; OR is parallel to tangent at P 131. $NP + PG = 2a$ 132. Arc $s = x^2/a$

If the line through O perpendicular to OP meets the tangent in U and the normal in H, $OU = r \tan \phi = r^2 d\theta/dr$ is the polar subtangent, $HO = r \cot \phi = dr/d\theta$ the polar subnormal, PU the polar tangent, and PH the polar normal. Find curves such that (133–138):

133. $HO = k^2 OU$ 134. $OU/HO = y^2/x^2$ 135. $PH = a$

136. H describes the line $r \cos \theta = p$ **137.** $s = \sqrt{(r^2 + 2ar)}$

138. $\phi = m\theta$

Find the orthogonal trajectories of the following families of plane curves in which the parameter is α (139–157):—

139. $x^3 - 3xy^2 = \alpha$ **140.** $y^2 = \alpha x$ **141.** $x^2 + \alpha y^2 = a$

142. $x^2 - y^2 + 2\alpha xy = a^2$ **143.** $x(x^2 + y^2) + \alpha(x^2 - y^2) = 0$

144. $(x^2 - a)^2 + (y^2 - b)^2 = \alpha^2$ **145.** $xy = \alpha(x - 1)^2$

146. $y = \alpha \log | x |$ **147.** $y = \alpha(x + a)e^x$

148. $\tanh^2 x + \tanh^2 (y + \alpha) = 1$ **149.** $x^2/\alpha + y^2 = a^2/(\alpha - 1)$

150. Rectangular hyperbolas through $(a, 0)$ with y-axis as asymptote

151. Ellipses, centre O, common major axis $2a$ along Ox

152. Conics circumscribing rectangle of angular points $(\pm a, \pm b)$

153. Parabolas with common focus O and latus rectum $2l$

154. $r = \tan (\theta + \alpha)$ **155.** $(r^2 + a^2) \sin \theta + \alpha r = 0$

156. $r = \alpha/(1 + 2 \cos \theta)$ **157.** $r = \alpha(1 + 2 \cos \theta)$

Find the trajectories at angle ω ($\tan \omega = m$) of 158–160:

158. $x^2 - y^2 = \alpha$ **159.** $x^2 + y^2 = 2\alpha x$ **160.** $r^p = \alpha \cos p\theta$

Integrate 161 and 162, and consider the run of their integral curves near the origin:

161. $y' = (y - x^2)/mx$ **162.** $y' = (y^2 - x)/y$

Solve 163–166 for y' and integrate:

163. $xy'^2 - 2yy' - x = 0$ **164.** $\cos x\, (dx^2 - dy^2) = 2 \sin x\, dxdy$

165. $(y' - x)^2 = y' + x$ **166.** $x^2y'^2 - xyy' + y^2 = 0$

Obtain the singular solutions of $y = px + f(p)$ when $f(p)$ has the forms (167–176):

167. p^3 **168.** $p/(p + 1)$ **169.** $2\sqrt{(ap)}$ **170.** $\sqrt{(p^2 - 1)}$

171. $\frac{2}{3}(p + 1)^{3/2}$ **172.** $\sqrt{\{(a + 2hp + bp^2)/(ab - h^2)\}}$

173. $ap/\sqrt{(1 + p^2)}$ **174.** $p - p \log | p |$

175. $\sqrt{(1 - p^2)} - p \text{ arc cos } p$

176. $\sqrt{(p^2 + 1)} - p \log \{p + \sqrt{(p^2 + 1)}\}$

177. $y = 3px + p^{-1}y^{-4}$ [Substitute $y^3 = v$] **178.** $y = p + e^x/p$

179. Transform $(1 + p^2)y^2 = f(x + py)$ by the substitution $2z = x^2 + y^2$, and hence integrate

180. Singular solution of $(1 + p^2)y^2 = (x + py)^3$

181. $x^4p^3 - x^3yp^2 - x^2y^2p + xy^3 = 1$ [Substitute $y = vx$, $x^2 = t^{-1}$]

182. $y = 2xp + p^2$ **183.** $y = x + ap - a \log | p |$

184. $x - y = 2ap - ap^2$ **185.** $3p^2y = (2p^3 - 1)x$

186. $y = p^2 + p^3$ 187. $y = yp^2 + 2px$ 188. $y = xp^2 + 2p$

189. $y = xp^2 + p^3$ 190. $(p - x)^3 + p(p - x) = 1$

191. $a^2(p - b)^2 + p(y + bx)^2 = 0$

192. Show that if $x + yp = f(p)$, then

$$y = \{C + \int f'(\tan t) d(\sec t)\} \cos t$$

where $\tan t = p$. Integrate $x + yp = p^3$

193. Integral curves of $r'^2 \sin\theta - 2rr' \cos\theta - r(r \sin\theta + a) = 0$

Writing $y = tp$, express x and y in terms of t (194–197):

194. $(y + p)^2 = y - p$ 195. $(y + p)^4 = 3y + p$

196. $y^3 - 3yp + p^3 = 0$ 197. $y^4 + p^4 = yp(y + p)$

198. $(p - 1)(y - 2x)^2 = p^2$ [Substitute $y - 2x = tp$]

199. Determine the constants a, m, n such that $y^2p^2 + 2xyp + ay^2 + 2mx + n = 0$ shall have a real singular solution. Integrate completely in this case

200. Integral curves and p-discriminant locus of

$$y^2 - x^2 - 2xyp + m^2\{(x + yp)^2 - a^2\} = 0$$

201. $y'' + y'^2 = 1$ 202. $y'' + (x - a)y'^3 = 0$

203. $2yy'' = y'^2$ 204. $xy^2y'' - xyy'^2 + (y^2 + a)y' = 0$

205. $yy'' = y'^2 - y'^3$ 206. $yy'' + y'^2 + 2a^2y^2 = 0$

207. $y''(y - 1) = 2y'^2$ 208. $yy'' + \frac{1}{2}y'^2 = y^{-2}$

209. $xyy'' + ny'(xy' - y) = 0$ 210. $x^2yy'' = 2(xy')^2 + axyy' + ay^2$

211. $(2yy'' - y'^2)x^2 + y^2 = 0$ 212. $x(1 - x)y'' + 2(1 - x)y' = 1$

213. Show that the form of the general integral of $yy'' = (a + 1)y'^2 + byy' + cy^2$ depends on the nature of the roots of $au^2 + bu + c = 0$ and integrate in the usual three cases

214. Show that $(y - x)y'' + F(y') = 0$ has a first integral of the form $(y - x)\ f(y') = A$. Integrate when

$$F(p) = (1 + p)(1 + p^2)$$

215. Show that $yy'' = my'^2 + ayy' + by^2 + cy^{m+1}$ may be reduced to linear form by a substitution $y = u^a$ (or $y = e^u$ if $m = 1$). Hence integrate 216–219:

216. $yy'' = 2y'^2 - 2y^3$ 217. $2yy'' = 6y'^2 + y^2 - 3y^4$

218. $yy'' = y'^2 + yy'$ 219. $3yy'' = 2y'^2 + 36y^2$

Find two-parameter families of curves such that (219–224):

220. $s = OT$ 221. $PG^3 = k\rho$ 222. $\rho \cos^2\psi = a$ 223. $\rho = TG$

224. Ordinate through T bisects radius of curvature

225. Find the inverses (with respect to the unit circle, centre O) of the integral curves of $rr'' = 2r'^2 + r^2 - 2r^3 \sec^3\theta$

226. Form the linear equation whose general integral is $y = A(1+x)^m + B(1-x)^m$

Show that 227–229 have a polynomial particular solution and deduce the general integral:

227. $xy'' - (x+3)y' + y = 0$ **228.** $(1+x^2)y'' - 2y = 0$

229. $x(x-1)y'' + (2x-1)y' - 6y = 0$

230. $x(1+x)y'' = \{(n-2)x + n\}y' + ny$ [part. sol. $y = 1/(1+x)$]

231. $x(1-x)^2 y'' = 2y$ [part. sol. $y = x/(1-x)$]

232. $y'' + 3y' + 2y = e^x + \sin x$ **233.** $y'' - 3y' - 4y = 10 \cos 2x$

234. $y'' + 2y' + 5y = 8 \sinh x$ **235.** $y'' + 6y' + 9y = e^{-3x} \cosh x$

236. $y'' - 5y' + 6y = 4x^2 e^x$ **237.** $y'' + 2y' + 3y = e^{-x} \cos x$

238. $y'' - 4y' + 4y = e^{2x} \cos^2 x$ **239.** $y''' - 3y' + 2y = x^2 e^x$

240. $y'' - 2y' \sin \alpha + y = 2 \cos \alpha \sin x$ $(\alpha \neq n\pi/2)$

241. $y'' \cos^2 \alpha - y' \sin 2\alpha + y = x^2 e^{x \tan \alpha}$

242. $y^{\text{iv}} + 2y^{\text{ii}} + y = 24x \sin x$ **243.** $y^{\text{vi}} - y^{\text{iv}} - y^{\text{ii}} + y = 4e^x$

Particular integral of $y'' + y = f(x)$ when $f(x)$ has the values (244–249):

244. $e^x \sin 2x$ **245.** $e^{2x} \cos x$ **246.** $e^x(x^2 - 1)$

247. $8 \cos x \cos 2x$ **248.** $4x \sin x$ **249.** $x \cos x - x^2 \sin x$

Ditto for $y'' - 2y' + y = f(x)$ (250–255):

250. $x^3 - 6x^2$ **251.** $e^x(1 + 2x + 3x^2)$ **252.** e^x/x^2

253. $e^x \sin x$ **254.** $50 \cosh x \cos x$ **255.** $8x^2 e^{3x}$

256. $y'' - 2y' + (1+m^2)y = (1+4m^2) \cos mx$ ($y = 1$, $y' = 0$ when $x = 0$)

257. $y'' + 3y' + 2y = 2xe^{-x}$ ($y = y' = 0$ when $x = 1$)

258. $y'' - 2ay' + (a^2 + m^2)y = 2me^{ax} \cos mx$ ($y = 0$, $y' = m$ when $x = 0$)

259. $y''' - y'' - y' + y = 8xe^{-x}$ ($y = y'' = 0$, $y' = 1$ when $x = 0$)

260. $y^{\text{iv}} - 2y'' + y = 12xe^x$ ($y = y'' = \frac{1}{2}$, $y' = 0$, $y''' = -3$ when $x = 0$)

261. $2x^2 y'' - xy' + y = x^2$ **262.** $x^2 y'' - 2xy' + 2y = 2x \log |x|$

263. $x^2 y'' + 4xy' + 2y = \log |1+x|$ **264.** $x^2 y'' + xy' + y = \log |x|$

265. $x^2 y'' - 2xy' + 2y = x^3 \sin x$

266. $2(x+1)^2 y'' - (x+1)y' + y = x$

267. $x^{a+1} y'' - (2a-1)x^a y' + a^2 x^{a-1} y = 1$ **268.** $4x^2 y'' + y = \sqrt{x}$

269. $x^2 y'' - 2nxy' + n(n+1)y = e^x x^{n+2}$

Transform 270–273 by the substitutions indicated, and integrate:

270. $y'' \cos x + y' \sin x = y \cos^3 x$ $[t = \sin x]$

271. $(1-x^2)y'' - xy' + y = 0$ $[x = \sin t]$

272. $(1+x^2)y''+xy'=4y$ $[x=\sinh t]$
273. $(1+x^2)^2y''+2x(1+x^2)y'+4y=0$ $[x=\tan \frac{1}{2}t]$
274. Find a substitution $t=\phi(x)$ such that the coefficients in $2p(x)y''+p'(x)y'+y=0$ become constants
275. $4xy''+2y'+y=0$
276. $y''\sin 2x+2y'\cos 2x+4y\operatorname{cosec} 2x=0$
277. Find a transformation $y=v\phi(x)$ by means of which $y''+p(x)y'+q(x)y=0$ takes the form $v''+r(x)v=0$
278. $x^2y''-2nxy'+\{n(n+1)+m^2x\}y=0$
279. $y''\sin^2 x-2y'\tan x+(2+\sin^2 x)y=0$
280. $y''\cos x+2y'\sin x-y\cos x=1+x$
281. Take y as independent variable in $y''+(e^{2y}+x)y'^3=0$ and integrate
282. Relation between p and q such that $y''+py'+qy=0$ shall have two real solutions (*a*) whose product is unity, (*b*) the sum of whose squares is unity
283. Verify when $p=1/x$
284. Solve $xy''+(\gamma-x)y'-\alpha y=0$ $(\gamma>\alpha>0)$ by definite integrals

Particular integrals of 285–287 by variation of parameters:

285. $y''+4y=2\tan x$ 286. $y''+y=\log|\cos x|$
287. $2x^2y''+7xy'+3y=\cos\sqrt{x}$

General integral of systems 288–293, where $\dot{x}=dx/dt$:

288. $\dot{x}+y=\sin 2t$, $\dot{y}-x=\cos 2t$
289. $\dot{x}=4x-2y+e^t$, $\dot{y}=6x-3y+e^{-t}$
290. $5\dot{x}+3\dot{y}-11x-7y=e^t$, $3\dot{x}+2\dot{y}-7x-5y=e^{2t}$
291. $7\dot{x}+\dot{y}+2x=E$, $\dot{x}+3\dot{y}+y=0$ $(x=y=0$ when $t=0)$ (*a*) when $E=30$, (*b*) when $E=29\sin t$
292. $5\ddot{x}+\dot{y}+2x=4\cos t$, $3\dot{x}+y=8t\cos t$ $(x=1,\ \dot{x}=0$ when $t=0)$
293. $\ddot{x}+3\dot{y}-4x+6y=10\cos t$, $\dot{x}+\ddot{y}-2x+4y=0$ $(x=y=0,\ \dot{x}=4,\ \dot{y}=2$ when $t=0)$

Solve 294–296 in series of ascending powers of x:

294. $(1-x^3)y''+6xy=0$ 295. $2x^2(1+x^2)y''+xy'-12x^2y=0$
296. $xy''+y'-4xy=0$ (solutions $y_1=u$ and $y_2=u\log x-v$)
297. Find a series solution of $xy''+(\gamma-x)y'-\alpha y=0$ such that $y=1$ when $x=0$. Denoting it by $F(\alpha;\gamma;x)$, show that a second solution is $x^{1-\gamma}F(\alpha-\gamma+1;\ 2-\gamma;\ x)$

298. Transform 297 by the substitution $y = e^x v$ and find a series for $e^{-x}F(\alpha;\ \gamma;\ x)$

299. Second solution of 297 when $\gamma = 1$

300. Show that $x^2y''' + 3xy'' + (1 - 4n^2 + 4x^2)y' + 4xy = 0$ is satisfied by the square of any solution of the Bessel Equation of order n, express $J_n(x)J_{-n}(x)$ as a power series

---

SOLUTIONS

1. $xy = C(x-1)(y+1)$ **2.** $1 + y = Cx^2(1-y)$

3. $x^3 + 3y + 6 \log | 1 - y | = C$ **4.** $e^{x^2} = Cx \cos y$

5. $y^2 + 1 = Cx/(x+1)$ **6.** $\sqrt{(x^2-1)} + \sqrt{(y^2-1)} = C$

7. $y = \tan (C + \text{arc} \sin x) = \{c\sqrt{(1-x^2)} + x\}/\{\sqrt{(1-x^2)} - cx\}$

8. $y = (C \cos^2 x - 1)/(C \cos^2 x + 1)$ **9.** $y = C(x^2 - x)/| x^2 - 1 |^{3/2}$

10. $x^2 + y^2 = \log \{Cx^2(1+y^2)\}$

11. $y + b = C\{x^2 + a^2 + x\sqrt{(x^2 + a^2)}\}$

12. $y + a \log (y^2 + a^2) = C + x - 1/x$ **13.** $x^2 = 2y^2 \log | Cy |$

14. $x^2 + y^2 = C(x+y)$ **15.** $y(y+3x)^5 = Cx^3$

16. $x^4 + 6x^2y^2 = Cy$ **17.** $x^2 = C^2 - 2Cy$

18. $y = C \exp (x^3/3ay^3)$ **19.** $(y-x)^{1-a} = Cxy$

20. $(x^2 + xy + y^2)^{1-a} = C(x-y)^{2+a}$ **21.** $e^{y/x}(x-y)^2 = Cx$

22. $y^a = Cx^b \exp \{x/y - y/x\}$

23. $(x-y)^2 \log | C(x-y) | = 4xy - 2x^2$

24. $\exp \tan (y/x) = C/x$ **25.** $(x - y + 1)(x + y + 2)^2 = C$

26. $(x + y - 1)^3 = C(x - y + 1)^2$

27. $2 \log (x^2 + y^2) + \text{arc} \tan (y/x) = C$

28. $(x - 2y + 11)^2 = C(2x + y + 2)$

29. $(x - 3y + 11)^4(x + y + 3)^3 = C$

30. $(x + 2y - 10)^5(x - y + 11)^3 = C$ **31.** $(x - 2y)^2 + 6x - 10y = C$

32. $(a+1)(y-x) + 2b \log |(a+1)(y+ax) + b(a-1)| = C$

33. $y - 4x - 1 = Cx^3(y - x - 1)$

34. $\log | y + a | + 2 \text{ arc} \tan \{(y+a)/(x+b)\} = C$

35. $(x-y)^2 + 3x + y + \frac{1}{2} \log | 2x - 2y + 1 | = C$

36. $x - y + \log \{(x+y)^2 + (x+y+2)^2\} = C$

37. $ax^2 + 2hxy + by^2 = C$

38. $x^3 + y^3 + 2x^2y = C$

39. $(x + y)(ax^2 + 2hxy + by^2) = C$

40. $2x^3y^2 - 4x^2y^3 + 5x^2y + 3xy = C$

41. $x^2 \log | y | = C$

42. $y \cos x - x \sin y = C$

43. $y + b = C(x + a)^2$

44. $1 + xy = C(x + y)$

45. $(x + y - 1)e^x = C$

46. $(x^3 + 7y^4)\sqrt{x} = C$

47. $x^2y^2 = \log Cy^2$

48. $\arcsin x + y\sqrt{(1 - x^2)} = C$

49. $ye^{xy} = C$

50. $(x + y) \sec y = C$

51. $x^3 + y^3 + 3xy = Cx^2$

52. $(x - y)e^{\frac{1}{2}(x+y)^2} = C$

53. $y(x + y)\sqrt{(x^2 + a^2)} = C$

54. $2x^3y^5 + x^{-2} - y^{-2} = C$

55. $e^y(x + y) = C(y + 1)$

56. $(x^3 + y)(x + y)^4 = C$

57. $y = Cx + \frac{1}{2}x^3 - 1$

58. $y = C/x + \frac{1}{2}x \log | x | - \frac{1}{4}x$

59. $y = C(x + 1) + x^4$

60. $y = C\sqrt{(x^2 + a)} + x$

61. $y\sqrt{(1 - x^2)} = C + \arcsin x$

62. $y\sqrt{\{(1 - x)/(1 + x)\}} = C + \arcsin x + \sqrt{(1 - x^2)}$

63. $y = C/\sqrt{(1 + x^2)} + x^2 - 2$

64. $y = C/\sqrt{x} + \sqrt{(1 + x)}$

65. $y\{x + \sqrt{(1 + x^2)}\} = C + x^2 + x\sqrt{(1 + x^2)} - \log \{x + \sqrt{(1 + x^2)}\}$

66. $y = [C + \frac{1}{2} \log \{\sqrt{x} + \sqrt{(x - 1)}\}]/\sqrt{(x^2 - x)} + \frac{1}{2}$

67. $y = x^{-1}(C + \log x) + \frac{1}{2}x + 1$

68. $y = C/\sqrt{(x^2 + x + 1)} + 2x - 3$

69. $y = \sqrt{(x^2 - 1)}[C + \log \{x + \sqrt{(x^2 - 1)}\}] - x$

70. $y = Cx\sqrt{(1 - x^2)} - x + x^3$

71. $(1 + x^2)y = C - \log | \cos x |$

72. $y\sqrt{(1 - x)} = C + \sqrt{(1 + x)}$

73. $y\sqrt{(1 - x)} = C + x^2$

74. $y = C(1 + x^2)^{-\frac{1}{2}} \exp \{-\arctan x\} + (x - 1)/(x^2 + 1)$

75. $y = x^{-2}(C + \sin x) - x^{-1} \cos x$

76. $y = (C + x) \cos x$

77. $y = C \cos x - 2 \cos^2 x$

78. $y = C \operatorname{cosec} 2x + \sec^2 x$

79. $y = Ce^{-\sin x} + \sin x - 1$

80. $y = (C + e^x) \sin x$

81. $y = Ce^x - x - 1 - \frac{1}{2}(\sin x + \cos x)$

82. $y = (C + 2x) \sec 2x + \tan 2x$

83. $y = Ce^{-2x} + \frac{1}{2}(x^2 - x) + \frac{1}{4} + 2 \cosh x - \sinh x$

84. $y = C \cos x + \sin x(1 + \frac{1}{2} \tan x)$

85. $y \cosh x = C + e^{3x} + 3e^x$

86. $y = C \tan x - \sec^2 x$

87. $y = (C + \log \sin x) \sec^3 x + \frac{1}{2} \sec x$

88. $y \tan x = C + \log \sin^2 x + \cos 2x$

89. $y \sin x = C - \frac{1}{8} \cos 4x - \frac{1}{4} \cos 2x + \frac{1}{2} \log | \tan \frac{1}{2}x |$

90. $y \cos x = C + \frac{1}{2} \log | \tan (\frac{1}{4}\pi + \frac{1}{2}x) | + \frac{1}{2} \cos x - \frac{1}{6} \cos 3x$

91. $y = \sqrt{(1 - x^2)}\{C + \log \sqrt{(1 - x^2)}\} + \arcsin x$

92. $y = Ce^x(1 + 1/x) - 1 - x$

93. $y = \{Cx^2 + 1\}^2$

94. $y^2 = x^3 + Cx + 1$

95. $y = x/(C - x^2)$

96. $y = \{C\sqrt{(1 + x^2)} + 1\}^{-1}$

97. $y = x^2\{C - x^2\}^{-\frac{1}{2}}$

98. $y = \{Cx + 1 + \log | x |\}^{-1}$

99. $y = \{Cx^2 + 2x\}^{-\frac{1}{2}}$

100. $y = x^{-2}\{Cx^{\frac{1}{2}} + 1\}^2$ 101. $y^3(x^3 + C) + 3x^2 = 0$
102. $y = \{C \sec^2 x + 2 \sec x \tan x\}^{-\frac{1}{2}}$ 103. $y = \{Ce^x + x + 1\}^{-2}$
104. $y^2 = (C + x^3 - x^2)/(x+1)$ 105. $y = 1 + 1/(Ce^x + x)$
106. $x^2y = x + 1 + 1/(Ce^{-2/x} - \frac{1}{2})$ 107. $y = x + 1/(Cx + ax^m)$
108. $y = x + 1/(Ce^{-x} + x - 1)$ 109. $y = x + a/\{C\sqrt{(x^2+a)} + 2x\}$
110. $y = x(Cx + \sin x)/(Cx - \sin x)$ 111. $x \sin(x+y) = C$
112. $y = x \tan(x + C)$
113. $y^2 = (1 - x^2)\{C + \log|1-x| - \log|1+x|\} + 2x$
114. $(1+x)y^2 = C - x^2 + x^3$ 115. $(x+y)^2 + 2 = C(x-y)^2$
116. $(x^2+y^2)^2 + 2a(x^2 - y^2) = C$ 117. $1 - a/r^2 = Ce^{2a\theta}$
118. $\log r^2 + a/r^2 = C + \cos 2\theta$ 119. $x^2 = y^2(C^2 - y^2)$
120. $y = x^2 \cos(x + C)$ 121. $y = (x^3 + Cx)/(Cx^2 + 1)$
122. Equation becomes $x^m z' = 2z$ (i) $y = x \coth(C - x)$, (ii) $y = x(1 + Cx^2)/(1 - Cx^2)$, (iii) $y = x \coth(x^{-1} + C)$
123. $xy = C$ 124. $2x^2 + y^2 = C^2$
125. $x + C = a \log\{a + \sqrt{(a^2 - y^2)}\} - a \log y - \sqrt{(a^2 - y^2)}$
126. $y = Cx^2 + 2a^2/3x$ 127. $y = a \cosh\{(x - C)/a\}$
128. $x^{\frac{2}{3}} + y^{\frac{2}{3}} = C$ 129. $y^2 = Ce^{x/a} + 4a(x + a)$
130. $y = Cx + ax \log|x| - b$ 131. $(a-y)(2a+y)^2 = 9a(C \pm x)^2$
132. $ay = C + \frac{1}{2}x\sqrt{(4x^2 - a^2)} - \frac{1}{4}a^2 \log\{2x + \sqrt{(4x^2 - a^2)}\}$
133. $r = Ce^{\pm k\theta}$ 134. $r = C \sin\theta$ and $r = C \operatorname{cosec}\theta$
135. $r = a \sin(\theta + C)$ 136. $r = C + p \log|\tan \frac{1}{2}\theta|$
137. $(\theta + C)^2 = 1 + 2a/r$ 138. $r^m = C \sin m\theta$
139. $y^3 - 3x^2y = \beta$ 140. $y^2 + 2x^2 = \beta$
141. $x^2 + y^2 - 2a \log|x| = \beta$ 142. $(x^2+y^2)^2 = \beta + 2a^2(x^2 - y^2)$
143. $y(3x^2 + y^2) = \beta(x^2 + y^2)^3$ 144. $x^{2b}(y^2 - b)^a = \beta(x^2 - a)^b y^{2a}$
145. $y^2 + x^2 - 4x + \log(x+1)^4 = \beta$ 146. $2y^2 + x^2(\log x^2 - 1) = \beta$
147. $x + a + 1 = \beta \exp(\frac{1}{2}y^2 + x)$ 148. $y = \cosh x + \beta$
149. Self-orthogonal 150. $3a(y^2 - x^2) + 2x^3 = \beta$
151. $x^2 + y^2 = 2a^2 \log|\beta x|$ 152. $a^2 \log x^2 + b^2 \log y^2 = \beta + x^2 + y^2$
153. $\sqrt{(2r/l - 1)} - \arctan\sqrt{(2r/l - 1)} = \beta \pm \frac{1}{2}\theta$
154. $r - 1/r = \beta - \theta$ 155. $(r^2 - a^2)\cos\theta + \beta r = 0$
156. $r^2(\sin\theta - \frac{1}{2}\sin 2\theta) = \beta$ 157. $r = \beta\sqrt{(\sin\theta)} \sin\frac{1}{2}\theta$
158. $x^2 + 2mxy - y^2 = \beta$ 159. $x^2 + y^2 = 2\beta(x - my)$
160. $r^p = \beta \cos(p\theta + \omega)$
161. $y = C|x|^{1/m} - x^2/(2m-1)$ $(m \neq \frac{1}{2})$, $y = x^2(C - \log x^2)$ $(m = \frac{1}{2})$; $m > 0$ node, $m < 0$ col
162. $y^2 = Ce^{2x} + x + \frac{1}{2}$, limiting point 163. $x^2 - 2Cy = C^2$
164. $e^{2y} - 2Ce^y + C^2 \cos^2 x = 0$

165. $144(2y - x^2 - x + C)^2 = (1 + 8x)^3$
166. $y^2 - 2Cy\sqrt{x} \cos(\frac{1}{2}\sqrt{3} \log x) + C^2x = 0$
167. $27y^2 + 4x^3 = 0$ 168. $(x + y)^2 + 2x - 2y + 1 = 0$
169. $xy + a = 0$ 170. $y^2 = x^2 - 1$ 171. $y = \frac{1}{3}x^3 - x$
172. $ax^2 + 2hxy + by^2 = 1$ 173. $x^{2/3} + y^{2/3} = a^{2/3}$
174. $y = e^x$ 175. $y = \sin x$ 176. $y = \cosh x$
177. $y^3 = Cx + 3/C$ [Singular Solution $y^6 = 12x$]
178. $y = Ce^x + 1/C$ [S.S. $y^2 = 4e^x$]
179. $(x - C)^2 + y^2 = f(C)$; also S.S.
180. $27(x^2 + y^2)^2 - 4x(x^2 + 9y^2) + 4y^2 = 0$
181. $x^2 - 2C^2xy + C^3 = 0$ [S.S. $32xy^3 = 27$]
182. $(xy + C)^2 = 4(y + x^2)(y^2 - Cx)$
183. $y + C = e^{(x+C)/a}$ [S.S. $y = x + a$]
184. $(x + C)^2 = 4a(y + C)$ [S.S. $y = x - a$]
185. $(3Cy + 1)^2 = 4C^3x^3$ [S.S. $y + x = 0$]
186. $(2x + C)^3 + (2x + C)^2 - 18(2x + C)y = 27y^2 + 16y$
187. $y^2 = 2Cx + C^2$
188. $x(1 - p)^2 = C + 2 \log p - 2p$,
$y(1 - p)^2 = (C - 4 + 2 \log p)p^2 + 2p$ [S.S. $y = x + 2$]
189. $x(1 - p)^2 = C + \frac{3}{2}p^2 - p^3$, $y(1 - p)^2 = Cp^2 + p^2 - \frac{1}{2}p^4$
[S.S. $y = x + 1$]
190. $p = x + t$; $x = t^{-1} - t - t^2$, $y = C + \frac{1}{2}t^{-2} - \log|t| - t + \frac{1}{3}t^3 + \frac{1}{2}t^4$
191. $(x - C)(y + bC) = a^2$ [S.S. $y + bx = \pm 2a\sqrt{b}$]
192. $x = 2 \tan t - C \sin t$, $y = \tan^2 t - 2 + C \cos t$
193. Cardioids $r = a \operatorname{cosec} \alpha \sin^2 \frac{1}{2}(\theta - \alpha)$ enveloped by the circle $r + a \sin \theta = 0$
194. $x = C + \log\{(t + 1)^2|t - 1|\}$, $y = (t^2 - t)/(t + 1)^2$
195. $x = C + \frac{4}{3} \log|t + 1| - \frac{1}{9} \log|3t + 1|$, $y = t(3t + 1)^{1/3}/(t + 1)^{4/3}$
196. $x = C - t + 3\int dt/(t^3 + 1)$, $y = 3t^2/(t^3 + 1)$
197. $x = C - t - \log|t + 1| + 4\int dt/(t^4 + 1)$, $y = (t^3 + t^2)/(t^4 + 1)$
198. $y = C + x + 1(C - x)$ [S.S. $y = 2x \pm 2$]
199. $a = -1$, $m = 0$, $n > 0$; $y^2 = n + Cx + \frac{1}{4}C^2$ [S.S. $x^2 + y^2 = n$]
200. Circles $x^2 + y^2 - 2Cx = m^2(a^2 - C^2)$ enveloped by the conic $(m^2 - 1)x^2 + m^2y^2 = m^4a^2$; tac-locus $y = 0$
201. $y = \log|Ae^x + Be^{-x}|$ 202. $x = Ae^y + Be^{-y} + a$
203. $y = (A + Bx)^2$ 204. $Ay^2 + a = Bx^A$
205. $y + A \log|y| + B = x$ 206. $y^2 = A \cos 2ax + B \sin 2ax$
207. $y = (A + x)/(B + x)$
208. $4(Ay - 2)(Ay + 4)^2 = 9A^4(x + B)^2$ [1st Int. $(yy')^2 = Ay - 2$]

209. $y^{n+1}=Ax^{n+1}+B$ [when $n=-1$, $y=Ax^B$]

210. $y=1/(Ax+Bx^{\alpha})$ **211.** $y=x(A+B\log|x|)^2$

212. $y=A+B/x+\{(1-x)/x\}\log|1-x|$

213. (i) real roots m and n, $y=\{Ae^{-max}+Be^{-nax}\}^{-1/a}$; (ii) $n=m$, $y=e^{mx}(A+Bx)^{-1/a}$; (iii) complex roots $h\pm ki$, $y=Ae^{hx}|\cos ka(x-B)|^{-1/a}$

214. $(x-B)^2+(y-B)^2=A^2$ **215.** $\alpha=1/(1-m)$

216. $y=1/(x^2+Ax+B)$ **217.** $y=1/\sqrt{(A\cos x+B\sin x+3)}$

218. $y=A\exp(Be^x)$ **219.** $y=(Ae^{2x}+Be^{-2x})^3$

220. $A^2y^2-\log y^2=4A(x+B)$ **221.** $Ay^2+(Ax-B)^2=k$

222. $y=a\cosh(A+x/a)+B$ **223.** $A^2y^2=1+Be^{ax}$

224. $x=A(t+\frac{1}{2}\sin 2t)+B$, $y=A\sin^2 t$ $(p=\tan t)$

225. $r=A\cos\theta+B\sin\theta+\sec\theta$

226. $(1-x^2)y''+2(m-1)xy'-m(m-1)y=0$

227. $y=A(x+3)+Be^x(x^2-4x+6)$

228. $y=A(1+x^2)+B\{x+(1+x^2)\text{ arc tan }x\}$

229. $y=(6x^2-6x+1)(A+B\log|1-1/x|)+B(6x-3)$

230. $y=(A+Bx^{n+1})/(1+x)$

231. $y=Ax/(1-x)+B\{x+1+2x\log|x|/(1-x)\}$

232. $y=Ae^{-x}+Be^{-2x}+\frac{1}{6}e^x+\frac{1}{10}\sin x-\frac{3}{10}\cos x$

233. $y=Ae^{-x}+Be^{4x}-\frac{4}{5}\cos 2x-\frac{3}{5}\sin 2x$

234. $y=e^{-x}(A\cos 2x+B\sin 2x-1)+\frac{1}{2}e^x$

235. $y=e^{-3x}(A+Bx+\cosh x)$

236. $y=Ae^{2x}+Be^{3x}+e^x(2x^2+6x+7)$

237. $y=e^{-x}(A\cos x\sqrt{2}+B\sin x\sqrt{2}+\cos x)$

238. $y=e^{2x}(A+Bx+\frac{1}{4}x^2-\frac{1}{8}\cos 2x)$

239. $y=Ae^{-2x}+e^x(B+Cx+\frac{1}{27}x^2-\frac{1}{27}x^3+\frac{1}{36}x^4)$

240. $y=e^{x\sin\alpha}\{A\cos(x\cos\alpha)+B\sin(x\cos\alpha)\}+\cot\alpha\cos x$

241. $y=e^{x\tan\alpha}\{A\cos x+B\sin x+(x^2-2)\sec^2\alpha\}$

242. $y=(A+Bx-3x^2)\cos x+(A_1+B_1x-x^3)\sin x$

243. $y=(A+Bx+\frac{1}{4}x^2)e^x+(A_1+B_1x)e^{-x}+C\cos x+C_1\sin x$

244. $-\frac{1}{10}e^x(\sin 2x+2\cos 2x)$ **245.** $\frac{1}{8}e^{2x}(\cos x+\sin x)$

246. $e^x(\frac{1}{2}x^2-x)$ **247.** $2x\sin x-\frac{1}{2}\cos 3x$

248. $x\sin x-x^2\cos x$ **249.** $\frac{1}{6}x^3\cos x$ **250.** $x^3-6x-12$

251. $e^x(\frac{1}{2}x^2+\frac{1}{3}x^3+\frac{1}{4}x^4)$ **252.** $-e^x\log|x|$

253. $-e^x\sin x$ **254.** $-25e^x\cos x+e^{-x}(3\cos x-4\sin x)$

255. $e^{3x}(2x^2-4x+3)$ **256.** $y=\cos mx+2m(e^x-1)\sin mx$

257. $y=e^{-x}(x-1)^2$ **258.** $y=(x+1)e^{ax}\sin mx$

259. $y=(x-1)e^x+(x+1)^2e^{-x}$ **260.** $y=e^{-x}+\frac{1}{2}e^x(x-1)^2$

261. $y = Ax + B\sqrt{x} + \frac{1}{3}x^2$

262. $y = Ax^2 + x\{B - \log x^2 - (\log | x |)^2\}$

263. $y = A/x + B/x^2 + \frac{1}{2}(1 + 1/x)^2 \log | 1 + x | - \frac{3}{4}$

264. $y = A \cos (\log | x |) + B \sin (\log | x |) + \log | x |$

265. $y = Ax^2 + Bx - x \sin x$

266. $y = \{A + \log | x + 1 |\}(x + 1) + B\sqrt{(x + 1)} - 1$

267. $y = x^a\{A + B \log | x |\} + x^{1-a}/(2a - 1)^2$

268. $y = \sqrt{x}\{A + B \log | x | + \frac{1}{8}(\log | x |)^2\}$

269. $y = Ax^n + Bx^{n+1} + e^x x^n$ **270.** $y = Ae^{\sin x} + Be^{-\sin x}$

271. $y = Ax + B\sqrt{(1 - x^2)}$ **272.** $y = A(1 + 2x^2) + Bx\sqrt{(1 + x^2)}$

273. $y = \{A(1 - x^2) + Bx\}/(1 + x^2)$ **274.** $t = \int\{p(x)\}^{-\frac{1}{2}}dx$

275. $y = A \cos \sqrt{x} + B \sin \sqrt{x}$

276. $y = A \cos t + B \sin t$ $(t = \log | \tan x |)$

277. $\phi = \exp \{ -\frac{1}{2}\int p dx\}$; $r = q - \frac{1}{4}p^2 - \frac{1}{2}p'$

278. $y = x^n(A \cos mx + B \sin mx)$ **279.** $y = (A + B \tan x) \sin x$

280. $y = A \sin x + B(\cos x + x \sin x) - \frac{1}{2}(x + 1) \cos x$

281. $x = Ae^v + Be^{-v} + \frac{1}{3}e^{2v}$

282. $q' + 2pq = 0$, also (*a*) $q < 0$, (*b*) $q > 0$

283. (*a*) $q = -m^2/x^2$; $y = x^m$ and x^{-m}; (*b*) $q = m^2/x^2$,
$y = \cos (m \log | x |)$ and $\sin (m \log | x |)$

284. $y = \int e^{xt}t^{a-1}(t - 1)^{\gamma - a - 1}dt$. Terminals (0, 1), also $(-\infty, 0)$ if $x > 0$ or $(1, \infty)$ if $x < 0$

285. $\sin 2x \log | \cos x | - x \cos 2x$

286. $\log | \cos x | + \sin x \log | \tan (\frac{1}{4}\pi + \frac{1}{2}x) | - 1$

287. $\{4 \sin \sqrt{x}\}/x^{3/2} - \{2 \cos \sqrt{x}\}/x$

288. $x = A \cos t + B \sin t - \frac{1}{3} \cos 2t$, $y = A \sin t - B \cos t + \frac{1}{3} \sin 2t$

289. $x = A + (B + 4t)e^t - e^{-t}$, $y = 2A + \frac{3}{2}(B - 1 + 4t)e^t - \frac{5}{2}e^{-t}$

290. $x = Ae^{3t} + (B - t)e^{2t} - \frac{3}{2}e^t$, $y = -2Ae^{3t} - (B + 2 - t)e^{2t} + 2e^t$

291. (*a*) $x = 15 - 10e^{-t/4} - 5e^{-2t/5}$, $y = -10e^{-t/4} + 10e^{-2t/5}$;
(*b*) $x = \frac{1}{17}(\frac{116}{3}e^{-t/4} + \frac{85}{3}e^{-2t/5} + 21 \sin t - 67 \cos t)$,
$y = \frac{1}{17}(\frac{116}{3}e^{-t/4} - \frac{170}{3}e^{-2t/5} - 13 \sin t + 18 \cos t)$

292. $x = (1 - t^2) \cos t$, $y = 3(1 - t^2) \sin t + 14\, t \cos t$

293. $x = 2e^{2t} - 2 \cos t - 3t \sin t$, $y = t \cos t + (1 - 2t) \sin t$

294. $y_1 = 1 - x^3$; $y_2 = x - \frac{1}{2}x^4 - \frac{1}{14}x^7 - \frac{1}{35}x^{10} - \dots$
with $(r + 3)C_{r+3} = (r - 3)C_r$

295. $y_1 = 1 + 2x^2 + \frac{4}{7}x^4 - \frac{8}{77}x^6 + \frac{16}{385}x^8 - \dots$
with $(2r - 1)C_r = -(2r - 10)C_{r-2}$,
$y_2 = \sqrt{x}\{1 + \frac{5}{4}x^2 + \frac{5}{32}x^4 - \frac{5}{128}x^6 + \dots\}$
with $2rC_r = -(2r - 9)C_{r-2}$

296. $u = 1 + x^2 + x^4/(2!)^2 + x^6/(3!)^2 + \ldots$

$v = x^2 + (1 + \frac{1}{2})x^4/(2!)^2 + (1 + \frac{1}{2} + \frac{1}{3})x^6/(3!)^2 + \ldots$

297. $$F(\alpha;\ \gamma;\ x) = 1 + \frac{\alpha}{\gamma}x + \frac{\alpha(\alpha+1)}{2!\,\gamma(\gamma+1)}x^2 + \frac{\alpha(\alpha+1)(\alpha+2)}{3!\,\gamma(\gamma+1)(\gamma+2)}x^3 + \ldots$$

298. $F(\gamma - \alpha;\ \gamma;\ -x)$

299. $F(\alpha;\ 1;\ x)\log|x| + \Sigma C_r x^r$, where

$$C_r = \left\{\frac{1}{\alpha} + \frac{1}{\alpha+1} + \ldots + \frac{1}{\alpha+r-1} - \frac{2}{1} - \frac{2}{2} - \ldots - \frac{2}{r}\right\} \times \frac{\alpha(\alpha+1)\ldots(\alpha+r-1)}{(r!)^2} \quad (r \geqslant 1)$$

300. $\Sigma(-)^s(2s)!\,(\frac{1}{2}x)^{2s}/\{(s!)^2\Gamma(s+n+1)\Gamma(s-n+1)\}$

INDEX